CHAPTER 21
Numbers to 1,000

Make up a question about the numbers on the chart.

SCHOOL HOME CONNECTION

Dear Family,

Today we started Chapter 21. We will read, write, and use numbers to 1,000. Here is the math vocabulary and an activity for us to do together at home.

Love,

____

My Math Words

hundreds
tens
ones
one thousand

Vocabulary

hundreds, tens, and ones The value of the digits in 3-digit numbers.

247

hundreds	tens	ones
2	4	7

200 40 7

one thousand

1,000 ones
100 tens
10 hundreds

ACTIVITY

Have your child count out small objects such as paper clips into groups of 10. Have him or her form hundreds by putting ten groups of 10 into sandwich bags. When not enough groups of 10 are left to make another hundred, have your child put the remaining groups of 10 together and any extra paper clips in a third group. Have your child tell how many hundreds, tens, and ones there are and write the number.

Books to Share

To read about numbers with your child, look for this book in your local library.

Betcha!
by Stuart J. Murphy.
HarperCollins, 1997.

Visit *The Learning Site* for additional ideas and activities. www.harcourtschool.com

Name ______________________________

You can show 100 as **hundreds**, tens, or ones.

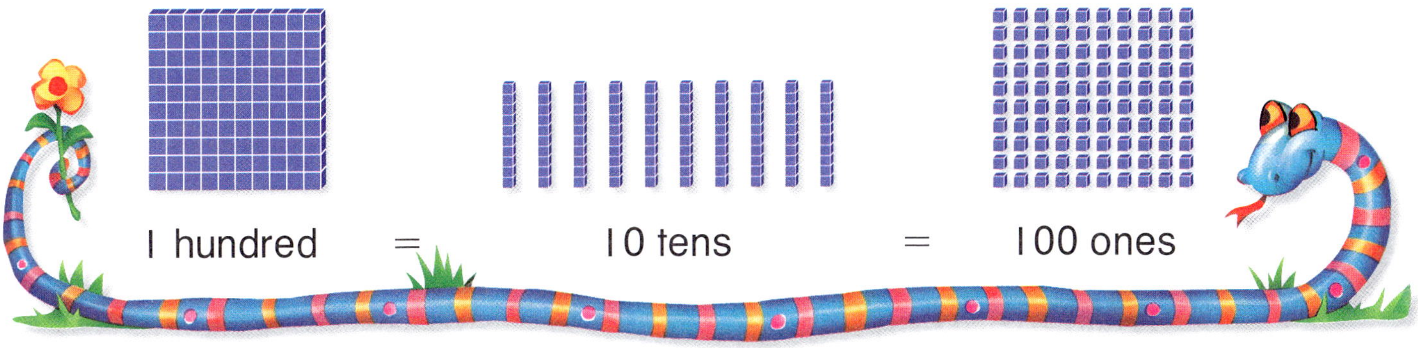

Write how many hundreds, tens, and ones.

1 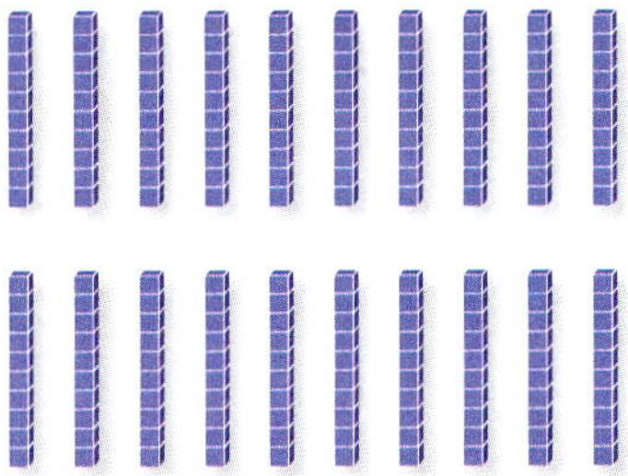

__2__ hundreds
__20__ tens
__200__ ones

2 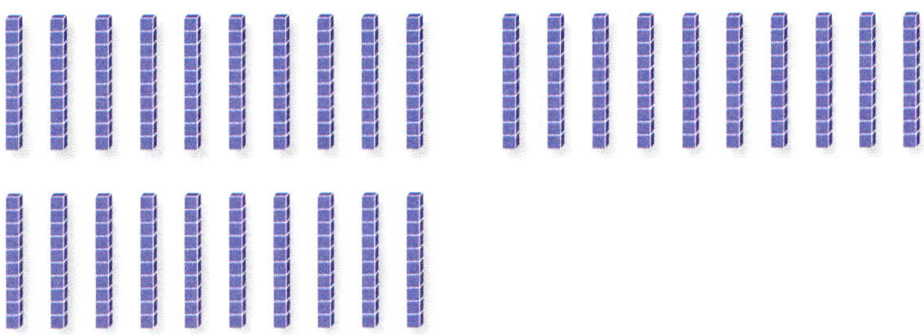

______ hundreds
______ tens
______ ones

3 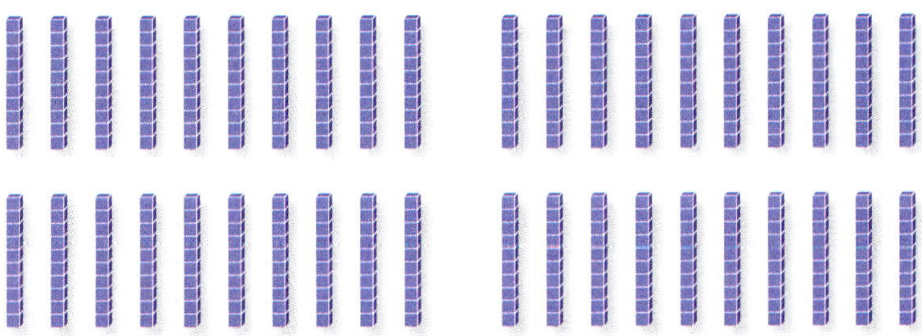

______ hundreds
______ tens
______ ones

4 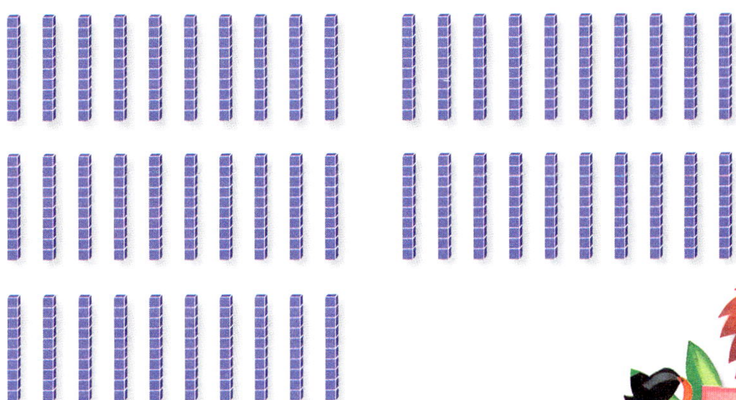

______ hundreds
______ tens
______ ones

Talk About It ■ **Reasoning**

What number is the same as 10 hundreds? How do you know?

Practice

Write how many hundreds, tens, and ones.

1 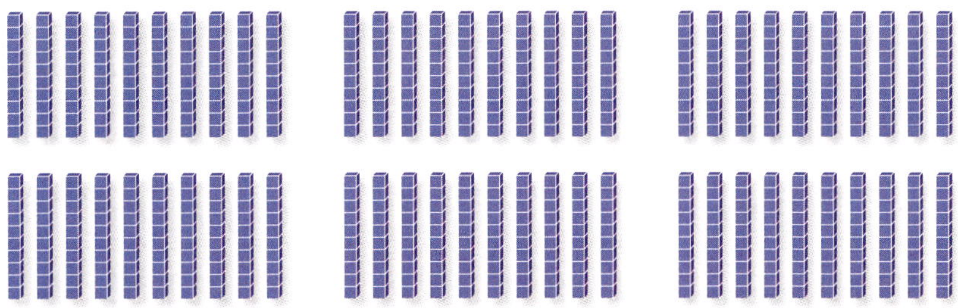

6 hundreds

60 tens

600 ones

2 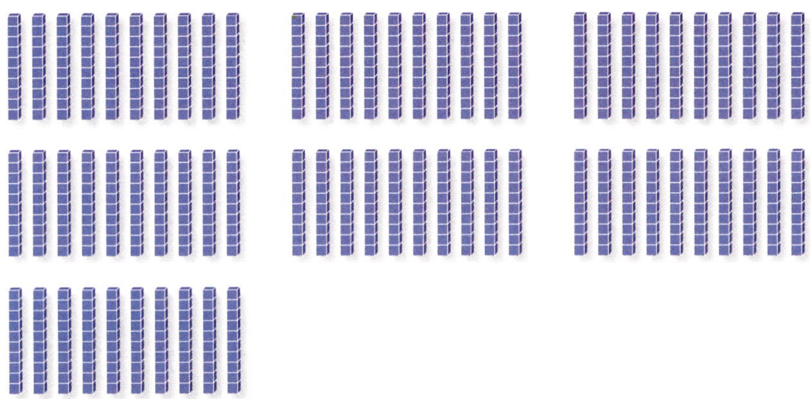

_____ hundreds

_____ tens

_____ ones

3 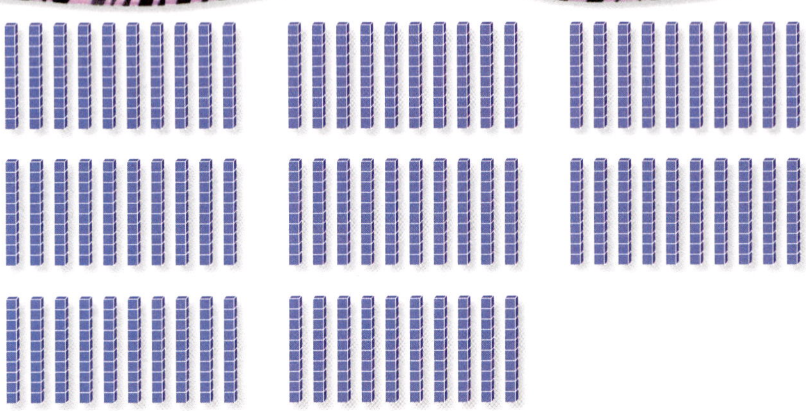

_____ hundreds

_____ tens

_____ ones

4 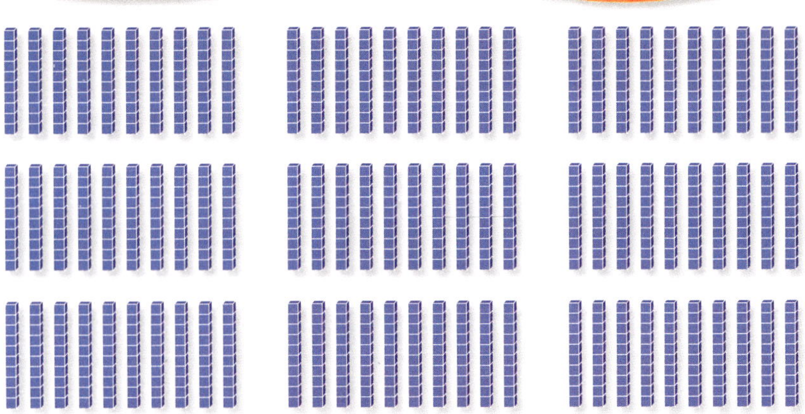

_____ hundreds

_____ tens

_____ ones

HOME ACTIVITY • Have your child count by tens to 100, and then by hundreds to 1,000.

Name ______________________________

Hundreds, Tens, and Ones

Write how many hundreds, tens, and ones.
Then write the number.

1

hundreds	tens	ones
3	0	5

305

2

hundreds	tens	ones

______

3

hundreds	tens	ones

______

4

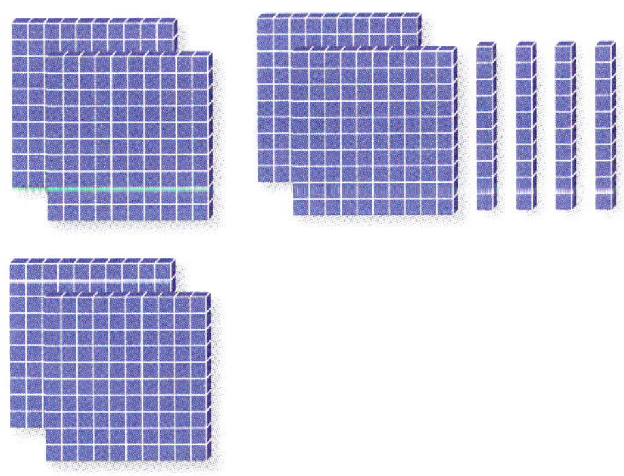

hundreds	tens	ones

______

5

hundreds	tens	ones

______

Talk About It ■ **Reasoning**

Why does 0 mean different things in the numbers above?

Practice

Write how many hundreds, tens, and ones.
Then write the number.

1

hundreds	tens	ones
3	1	4

314

2

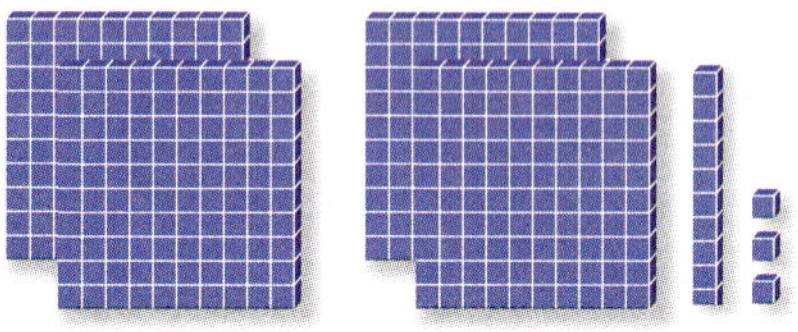

hundreds	tens	ones

______

3

hundreds	tens	ones

______

4

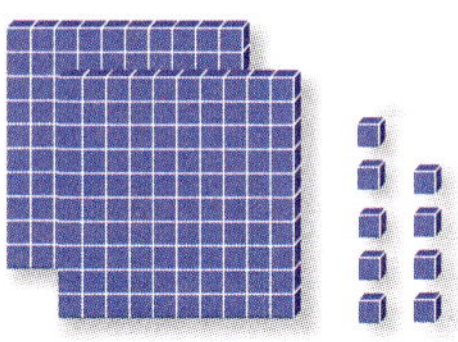

hundreds	tens	ones

______

Problem Solving ■ Number Sense

5 Show 999 using base ten blocks. Add 1.
What number is next? ______

How many hundreds does it take to make 1,000? ______

HOME ACTIVITY • Say a number between 100 and 1,000, and have your child tell how many hundreds, tens, and ones make up that number.

Name ______________________________

Place Value

What is the value of each digit in 258?

hundreds	tens	ones
	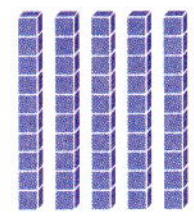	
2	5	8

2 hundreds	5 tens	8 ones
200	50	8

Circle the value of the blue digit.

1 634

600 60 6

2 903

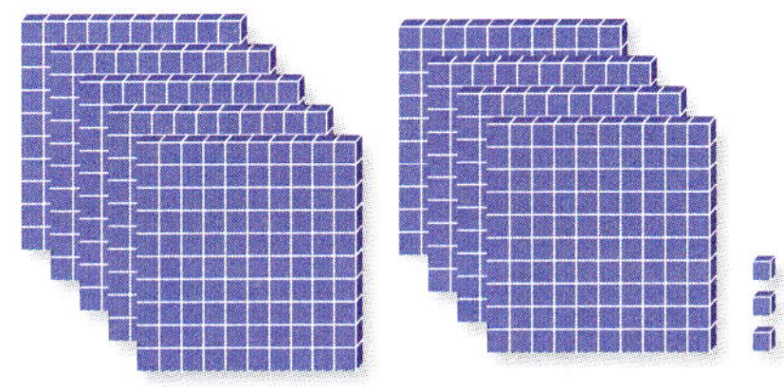

300 30 3

3 427

200 20 2

4 555

500 50 5

5 266

600 60 6

6 878

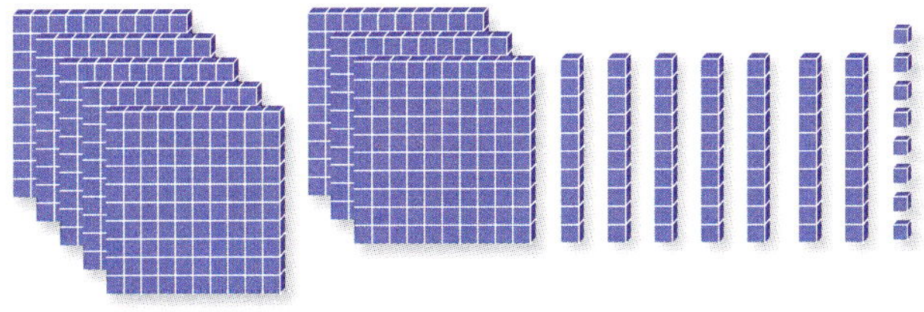

800 80 8

Talk About It ■ **Reasoning**

Ralph says 598 is larger than 621 because 598 has larger digits. What do you say?

Practice

hundreds	tens	ones
1	4	7

Circle the value of the blue digit.

1. 147
   400 40 4
2. 940
   900 90 9
3. 318
   800 80 8
4. 462
   200 20 2
5. 523
   500 50 5
6. 646
   600 60 6
7. 754
   500 50 5
8. 295
   900 90 9
9. 839
   800 80 8
10. 286
    200 20 2
11. 988
    800 80 8
12. 379
    900 90 9

Problem Solving ■ Estimation

Circle the reasonable estimate.

13. There are _______ children in my class.
    200 20 2,000
14. Andy has _______ sisters.
    3,000 30 3
15. The phone book has _______ pages.
    500 50 5,000
16. Wing hit _______ home runs in the baseball game.
    4,000 40 4

HOME ACTIVITY • Using a large book such as the phone book, pick any page and point out the page number. Ask your child to tell the value of the hundreds, tens, and ones digits.

Name ______________________________

Read and Write Numbers

hundreds	tens	ones
2	4	3

Numbers can be written in different ways.

two hundred forty-three

200 + 40 + 3

243

Read the number. Write it in different ways.

1 one hundred eighty-five

hundreds	tens	ones

_____ + _____ + _____

_____

2 five hundred nine

hundreds	tens	ones

_____ + _____ + _____

_____

3 three hundred sixty-seven

hundreds	tens	ones

_____ + _____ + _____

_____

4 eight hundred forty-six

hundreds	tens	ones

_____ + _____ + _____

_____

Talk About It ■ Reasoning

How do you know that 400 + 20 + 3 is the same as 423? Prove your answer.

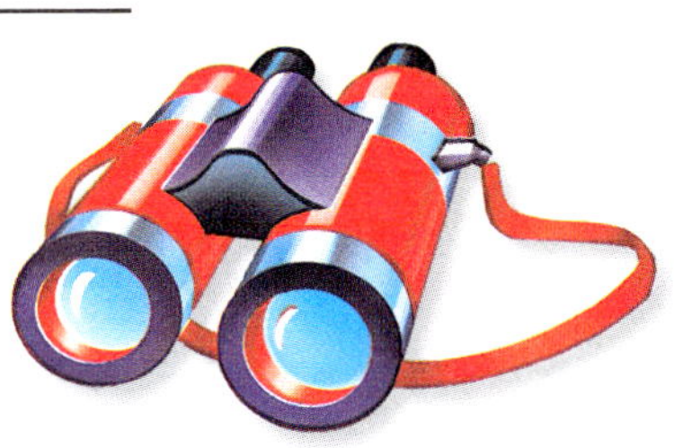

Practice

Read the number.
Write it in different ways.

1 three hundred fifty-one

hundreds	tens	ones
3	5	1

300 + 50 + 1

351

2 six hundred eighty

hundreds	tens	ones

______ + ______ + ______

______

3 four hundred thirty-nine

hundreds	tens	ones

______ + ______ + ______

______

4 seven hundred twelve

hundreds	tens	ones

______ + ______ + ______

______

Problem Solving • Application

Write the number to solve.

5 Pat has 6 bags with 100 marbles in each bag. He also has 4 loose marbles. How many marbles does he have altogether? Write an addition sentence to show the number.

______ + ______ + ______ = ______

HOME ACTIVITY • Name any number up to 1,000, such as six hundred fifty-eight. Have your child write that number with hundreds, tens, and ones (6 hundreds, 5 tens, 8 ones), in expanded notation (600+50+8), and as a number in standard form (658).

Name ______________________

UNDERSTAND > PLAN > SOLVE > CHECK

Problem Solving
Use a Table

This table tells the weight of some animals in the zoo.

Animal	Weight
zebra	765 pounds
bear	972 pounds
seal	217 pounds
tiger	455 pounds
chimpanzee	81 pounds

Use the table to answer the questions.

1. Which animal weighs 7 hundreds, 6 tens, and 5 ones? zebra

2. How much does the bear weigh? ______

3. Which animal has a weight of four hundred fifty-five pounds? ______

4. How much does a chimpanzee weigh? ______

5. Which animal weighs 200 + 10 + 7 pounds? ______

6. Name two animals which would weigh close to 1,000 pounds together. ______

Practice

This table tells how many kinds of animals and plants are endangered in the world.

Group	Number of Endangered Species
mammals	333
birds	273
reptiles	115
fish	122
plants	719

Use the table to answer the questions.

1. Which group has 3 hundreds, 3 tens, and 3 ones? mammals
2. How many kinds of fish are endangered? ____________
3. Which group has one hundred fifteen endangered species? ____________
4. How many kinds of plants are endangered? ____________
5. Which group has 200 + 70 + 3 endangered species? ____________

Math Journal

Write About It

Write some problems using the information in the table. Ask a classmate to solve your problems.

HOME ACTIVITY • With your child, find tables in the newspaper or in magazines. Talk about the information given in the tables.

Name ______________________

Review/Test
Chapter 21

CHECK ■ Concepts and Skills

Write how many hundreds, tens, and ones. Then write the number.

1 

hundreds	tens	ones

______

Circle the value of the blue digit.

2 248

400 40 4

3 886

800 80 8

4 507

700 70 7

Read the number. Write it in different ways.

5 two hundred thirty-seven

hundreds	tens	ones

______ + ______ + ______

______

6 nine hundred six

hundreds	tens	ones

______ + ______ + ______

______

CHECK ■ Problem Solving

Use the table to answer the questions.

Day of the Week	People at the Show
Friday	199
Saturday	475
Sunday	268

7 On which day were four hundred seventy-five people at the show?

______

8 Which two days together had about the same number of people as the other day?

______ ______

Name ______________________________

Standardized Test Prep
Chapters 1–21

Choose the best answer for questions 1–4.

1 Which tells the value of 1 in this number?

123

- ○ 1,000
- ○ 1
- ○ 10
- ○ 100

2 What tool would you use to find out how long your shoe is?

 ○

 ○

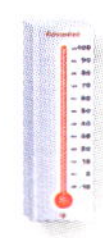 ○

 ○

3 Which does the model show?

- ○ 4 hundreds
- ○ 4 ones
- ○ 40 tens
- ○ 4 tens

4 Which group has two hundred forty-five students?

Number of Children	
Kindergarten	210
1st Grade	156
2nd Grade	245

- ○ Kindergarten
- ○ 1st Grade
- ○ 2nd Grade
- ○ 3rd Grade

Show What You Know

5 Draw blocks. Show hundreds, tens, and ones. Write the number in different ways.

hundreds	tens	ones

_____ + _____ + _____

_____

CHAPTER 22

Comparing and Ordering Numbers to 1,000

Tell about the numbers you see in this picture. Use the words before, after, and between.

SCHOOL HOME CONNECTION

Dear Family,
Today we started Chapter 22. We will compare and order numbers to 1,000. Here is the math vocabulary and an activity for us to do together at home.

Love,

____

My Math Words
greater than
less than
equal to

Vocabulary

greater than (>), **less than** (<), and **equal to** (=) Symbols used to compare two numbers.

$765 > 756$
765 is greater than 756.

$249 < 250$
249 is less than 250.

$542 = 542$
542 is equal to 542.

ACTIVITY

Write the numerals from 0 to 9 on slips of paper, making two "cards" for each number. Shuffle the cards, and deal three each, face up, to yourself and your child. Each of you should make the greatest 3-digit number possible. The player with the greater number keeps all six cards. Play until all the cards have been used.

Books to Share

To read about numbers with your child, look for these books in your local library.

The King's Chessboard,
by David Birch,
Penguin, 1993.

Beep Beep, Vroom Vroom!,
by Stuart J. Murphy,
HarperCollins, 2000.

Visit *The Learning Site* for additional ideas and activities. www.harcourtschool.com

Name ______________________________

100 Less, 100 More

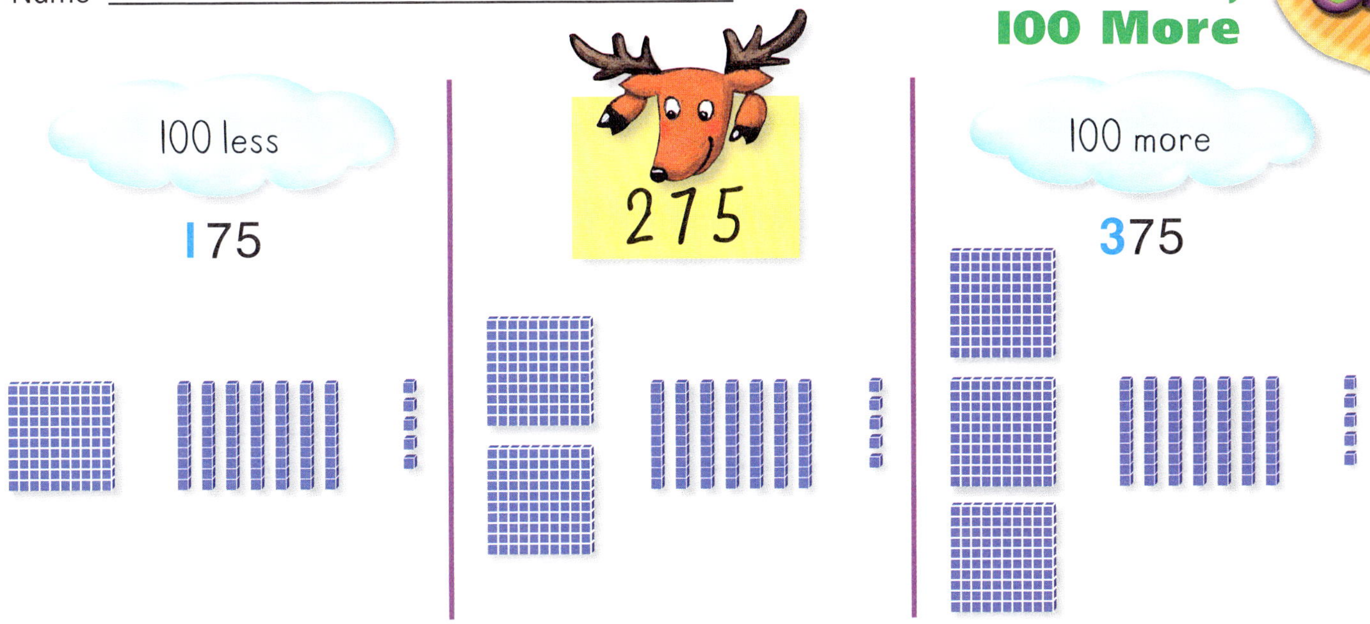

Use to compare.
Write the numbers that are 100 less and 100 more.

	100 less	Number	100 more
1	574	674	774
2	____	838	____
3	____	313	____
4	____	206	____
5	____	154	____
6	____	709	____

Talk About It ■ **Reasoning**

How would you write a number that is 200 more than 125? Why?

Practice

Use [hundreds block] [tens block] [ones block] to compare.
Write the numbers that are 100 less and 100 more.

	100 less	Number	100 more
1	306	406	506
2	______	222	______
3	______	705	______
4	______	391	______
5	______	608	______
6	______	838	______
7	______	150	______

Problem Solving ■ Number Sense

Count forward by hundreds. Write the numbers.

8. 75, 175, 275, ______, ______, ______, ______, ______

9. 202, 302, 402, ______, ______, ______, ______, ______

HOME ACTIVITY • Name any number between 100 and 900. Have your child name the number that is one hundred more and 100 less than that number. Repeat.

Name ______________________

Compare Numbers: >, <, and = (Algebra)

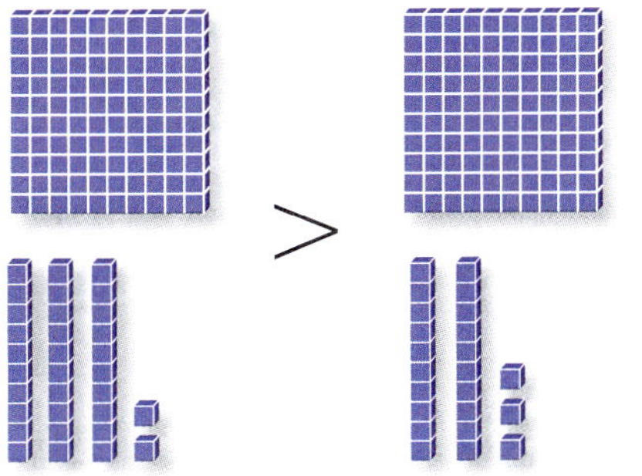

132 is greater than 123.

132 (>) 123

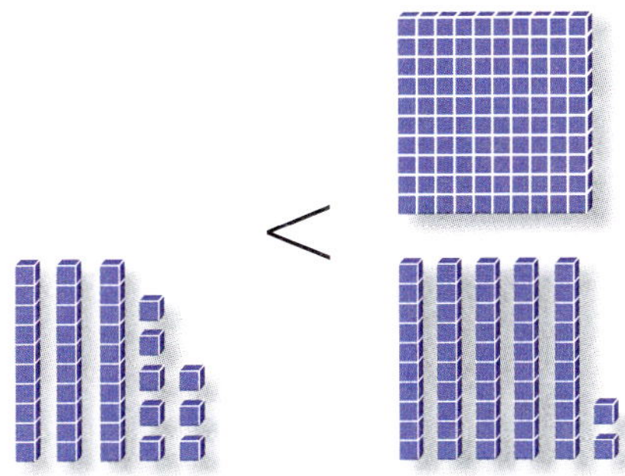

38 is less than 152.

38 (<) 152

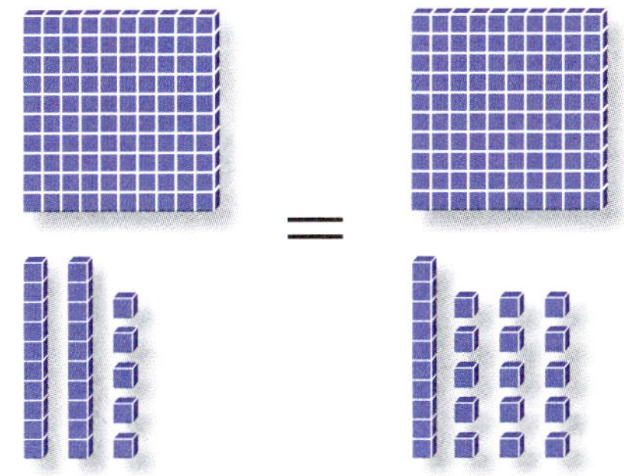

125 is equal to 125.

125 (=) 125

Write greater than, less than, or equal to.
Then write >, <, or =.

1

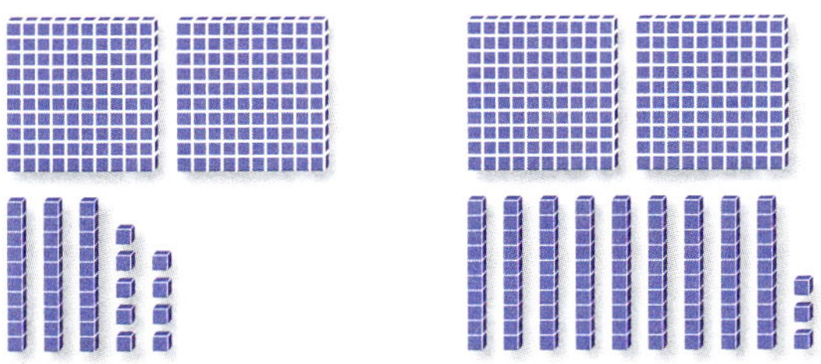

239 is less than 293.

239 (<) 293

2

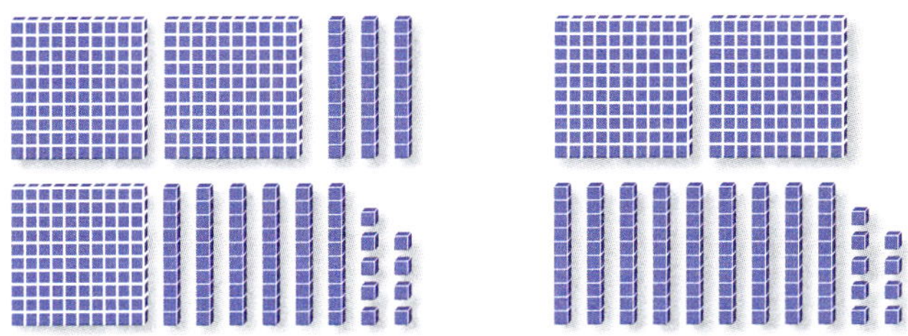

399 is ______________ 299.

399 ( ) 299

3

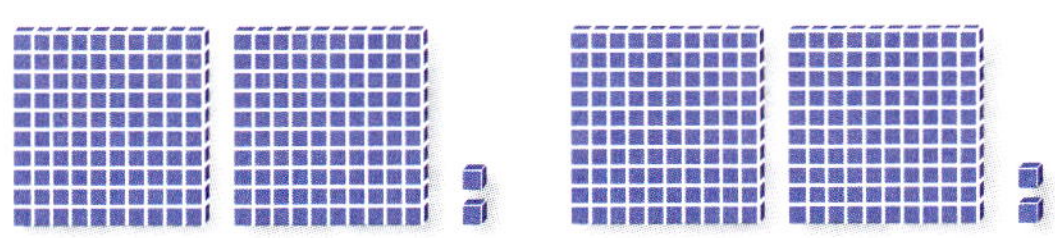

202 is ______________ 202.

202 ( ) 202

4

119 is ______________ 120.

119 ( ) 120

Talk About It ■ **Reasoning**

How is comparing numbers like looking up words in a dictionary?
How is it different?

Practice

Write greater than, less than, or equal to.
Then write $>$, $<$, or $=$.

1. 570 is greater than 57.
   570 $>$ 57

2. 256 is ______ 265.
   256 ○ 265

3. 606 is ______ 660.
   606 ○ 660

4. 100 is ______ 100.
   100 ○ 100

5. 840 is ______ 840.
   840 ○ 840

6. 799 is ______ 800.
   799 ○ 800

7. 36 is ______ 360.
   36 ○ 360

8. 699 is ______ 599.
   699 ○ 599

Problem Solving ▪ Mental Math

Write the number.

9. Ralph Raccoon invites 300 friends to a picnic. His friend Edie can't come. How many of Ralph Raccoon's friends come to the picnic?

   ______ friends

10. Ralph Raccoon counts 139 cups for his picnic. He has 1 more cup to count. How many cups does he have in all?

    ______ cups

HOME ACTIVITY • Show your child two 3-digit numbers, and have him or her tell you which is less.

Name ____________________

Order Numbers: Before, After, Between

Write the number that is just before, between, or just after.

	before	between	after
1	299, 300	299, 300, 301	234, 235
2	____, 825	519, ____, 521	100, ____
3	____, 601	333, ____, 335	969, ____
4	____, 150	698, ____, 700	609, ____
5	____, 777	997, ____, 999	499, ____
6	____, 568	448, ____, 450	327, ____

Talk About It ▪ Reasoning

How is finding numbers before, after, and between other numbers like counting? What number is just after 999?

Practice

Write the number that is just before, between, or just after.

1. 788, 789
2. 449, ______, 451
3. 299, ______
4. ______, 501
5. 99, ______, 101
6. 698, ______
7. 89, ______
8. ______, 350
9. ______, 400
10. 209, ______, 211
11. 767, ______
12. ______, 888
13. 329, ______
14. 89, ______, 91

Problem Solving ■ Reasoning

Choose your own way to solve this problem.

15. Emma has 537 stickers. Juan has 538 stickers. Chen has 539 stickers. Which number is closest to 639?

______

HOME ACTIVITY • Say any 3-digit number, and have your child tell you which number comes just before and just after.

Name ______________________________

Order Numbers on a Number Line

Algebra

Put the numbers in order from least to greatest. A number line can help you find the order.

311	301	308

300 301 302 303 304 305 306 307 308 309 310 311 312 313 314

301, 308, 311

Write the numbers in order from least to greatest.
Use the number line to help you.

650 651 652 653 654 655 656 657 658 659 660 661 662 663 664 665 666 667 668

1 657 651 661 ______, ______, ______

2 656 665 663 ______, ______, ______

3 659 650 654 ______, ______, ______

4 658 655 667 ______, ______, ______

Talk About It ■ Reasoning

How could you use the symbols > or < in the problems above?

Practice

Write the numbers in order from least to greatest.
Use the number line to help you.

420 421 422 423 424 425 426 427 428 429 430 431 432 433 434 435 436 437 438

1 427 422 435 431 — 422, 427, 431, 435

2 420 425 422 432 — ____, ____, ____, ____

3 420 423 430 432 — ____, ____, ____, ____

4 436 421 424 430 — ____, ____, ____, ____

5 425 433 437 429 — ____, ____, ____, ____

6 431 426 438 422 — ____, ____, ____, ____

Mixed Review

Write the total amount.

7

____ ¢

8

____ ¢

HOME ACTIVITY • Name any three numbers up to 999. Have your child write the numbers and then order them from least to greatest. Repeat with three different numbers.

Name ____________________

UNDERSTAND › PLAN › SOLVE › CHECK

Problem Solving
Find a Pattern

Pedro sees a pattern in the numbers 345, 445, 545.
He is going to write the next four numbers.
Can you guess Pedro's rule? What numbers will he write?

The rule could be count on by 100.

345, 445, 545, 645, 745, 845, 945

Find the pattern. Write the rule.
Continue the pattern.

1 Ann sees a pattern in the numbers 813, 823, 833.

The rule could be count ____________________.

813, 823, 833, ________, ________, ________, ________

---

2 Meg sees a pattern in the numbers 224, 222, 220.

The rule could be count ____________________.

224, 222, 220, ________, ________, ________, ________

3 Alvin sees a pattern in the numbers 705, 605, 505.

The rule could be count ____________________.

705, 605, 505, ________, ________, ________, ________

Practice

Find the pattern. Write the rule.
Continue the pattern.

1 Steffie sees a pattern in the numbers 364, 354, 344.

The rule could be count back by 10.

364, 354, 344, 334, 324, 314, 304

---

2 Ramesh sees a pattern in the numbers 441, 444, 447.

The rule could be count ______________.

441, 444, 447, ______, ______, ______, ______

---

3 Linda sees a pattern in the numbers 525, 530, 535.

The rule could be count ______________.

525, 530, 535, ______, ______, ______, ______

---

4 Bob sees a pattern in the numbers 973, 975, 977.

The rule could be count ______________.

973, 975, 977, ______, ______, ______, ______

Math Journal

Write About It

Al had $2.25, but he wanted to earn more money.
Mom said she would pay Al to brush the cat.
Al had $2.35 on Monday, $2.45 on Tuesday, and $2.55 on Wednesday. How much is Mom paying Al each day?

HOME ACTIVITY • With your child, look at the exercises in this lesson. Ask your child to explain how he or she decided what the rule was for each pattern.

Name ______________________________

CHECK ▪ Concepts and Skills

Review/Test
Chapter 22

Write the numbers that are 100 less and 100 more.

	100 less	Number	100 more
1	______	272	______
2	______	105	______

Write greater than, less than, or equal to.
Then write >, <, or =.

3. 303 is ______________ 330

303 ◯ 330

4. 789 is ______________ 789

789 ◯ 789

Write the number that is just before, between, or just after.

5. 659, ________, 661

6. ________, 423

7. 800, ________

Write the numbers in order from least to greatest.

675 676 677 678 679 680 681 682 683 684 685

8. 675 685 682 680

________, ________, ________, ________

CHECK ▪ Problem Solving

Find the pattern. Write the rule.
Continue the pattern.

9. Ed sees a pattern in the numbers 333, 331, 329.

The rule could be count ______________.

333, 331, 329, ________, ________, ________, ________

Name ______________________________

Standardized Test Prep

Chapters 1–22

Choose the best answer for questions 1–5.

1 68 ◯ 56

- ○ <
- ○ >
- ○ =
- ○ +

2 What number is just after 246?

- ○ 245
- ○ 240
- ○ 247
- ○ 250

3

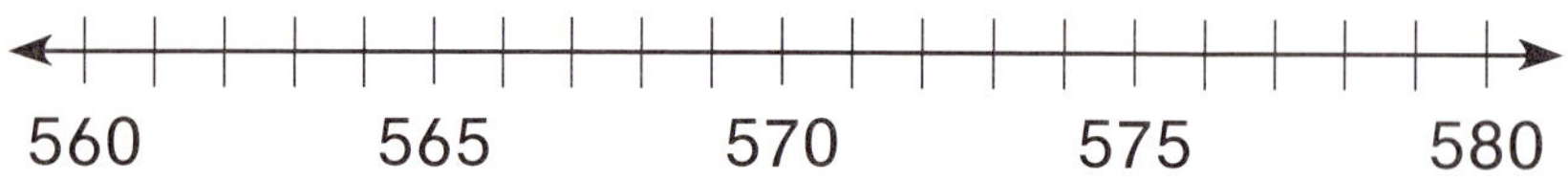

Which shows the numbers in order from least to greatest?

- ○ 579, 574, 565, 562
- ○ 574, 562, 565, 579
- ○ 562, 574, 565, 579
- ○ 562, 565, 574, 579

4 Which group of numbers shows the rule **count by 10**?

- ○ 625, 642, 679, 689
- ○ 602, 622, 642, 652
- ○ 645, 655, 665, 675
- ○ 645, 655, 660, 670

5 What is the value of the blue digit?

4**8**5

- ○ 80
- ○ 800
- ○ 8
- ○ 8,000

Show What You Know

6 In the boxes, write numbers that are greater than 100.
Then write the numbers that are 100 less and 100 more.

100 less		100 more
______	☐	______
______	☐	______

100 less		100 more
______	☐	______
______	☐	______

CHAPTER 23

Parts of a Whole

Color one part of each flag. Tell the fraction for the part you colored.

School Home Connection

Dear Family,

Today we started Chapter 23. We will look at fractions and learn to find equal parts of wholes. Here are the math vocabulary words and an activity for us to do together at home.

Love,

____

My Math Words

one-half
three-fourths

Vocabulary

one-half

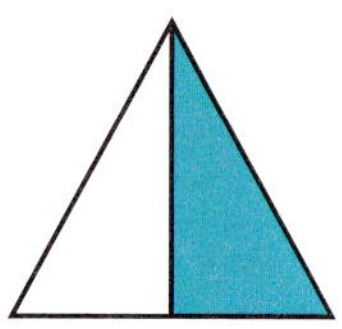

2 equal parts

$\frac{1}{2}$ is blue

three-fourths

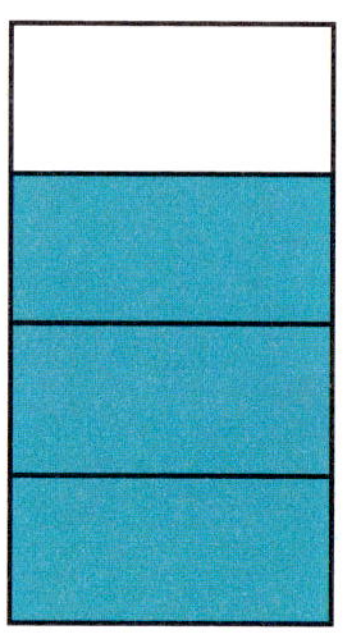

4 equal parts

$\frac{3}{4}$ is blue

Visit *The Learning Site* for additional ideas and activities. www.harcourtschool.com

Activity

Help your child learn about fractions at lunchtime. For example, you might cut a sandwich into 2, 3, or 4 equal pieces. After your child eats each piece, have him or her name the fraction of the sandwich that has been eaten and the fraction that is left.

Books to Share

To read about fractions with your child, look for these books in your local library.

A Birthday Cake for Little Bear,
by Max Velthuijs,
North-South Books Inc., 1988.

Give Me Half!,
by Stuart J. Murphy,
HarperCollins, 1998.

You need **equal parts** to show a **fraction**.

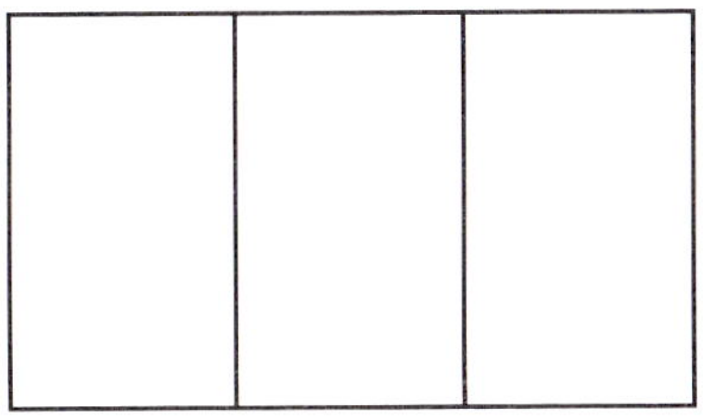

There are 3 equal parts.

Write the number of parts.
Are the parts equal? Circle yes or no.

1 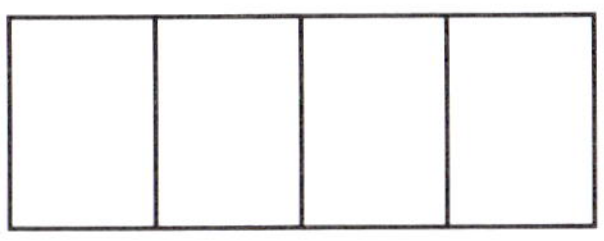
4 parts — (yes) / no

2 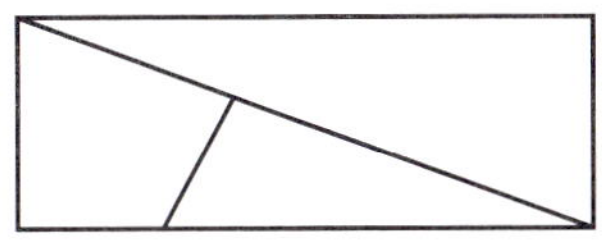
_____ parts — yes / no

3 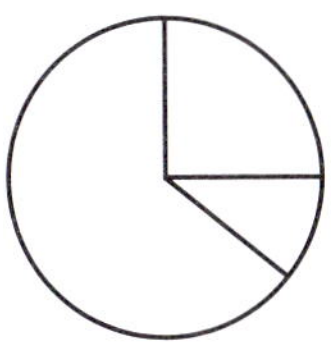
_____ parts — yes / no

4 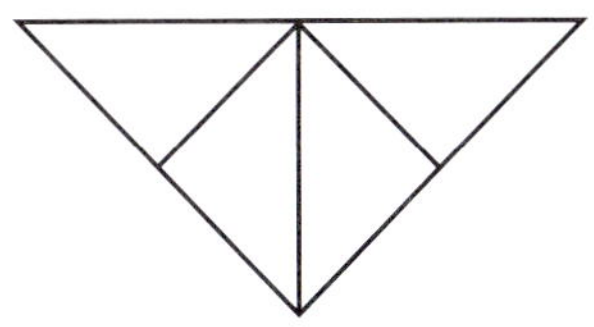
_____ parts — yes / no

5 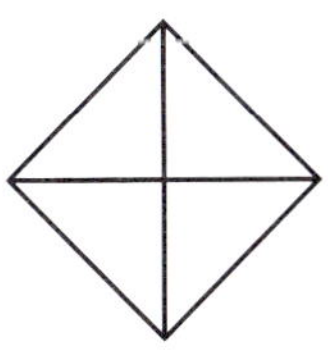
_____ parts — yes / no

6 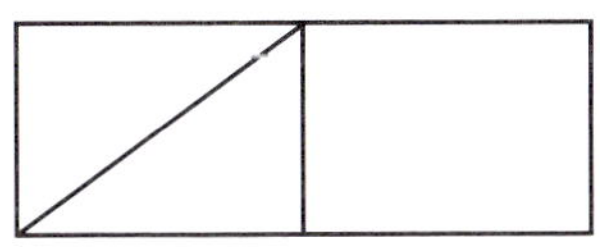
_____ parts — yes / no

7 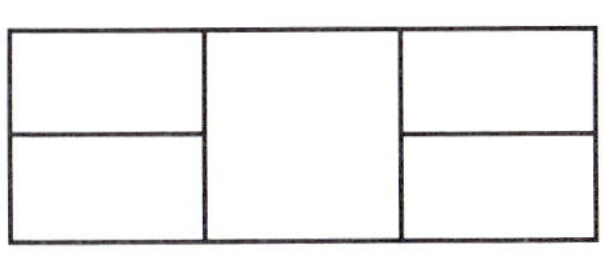
_____ parts — yes / no

8 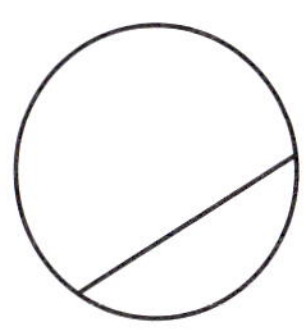
_____ parts — yes / no

Talk About It ▪ Reasoning

How can you tell if the parts are equal?

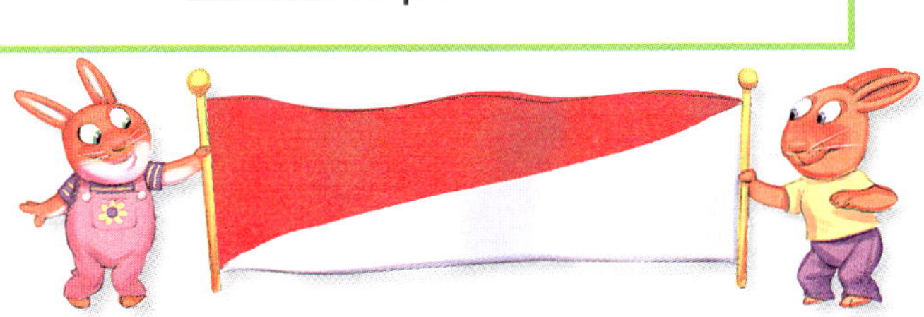

Practice

Write the number of parts.
Are the parts equal? Circle yes or no.

1. 
3 parts — yes / (no)

2. 
_____ parts — yes / no

3. 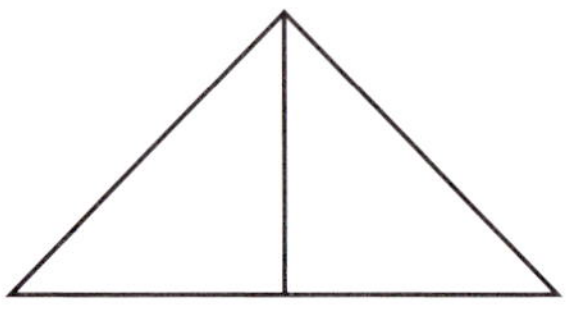
_____ parts — yes / no

4. 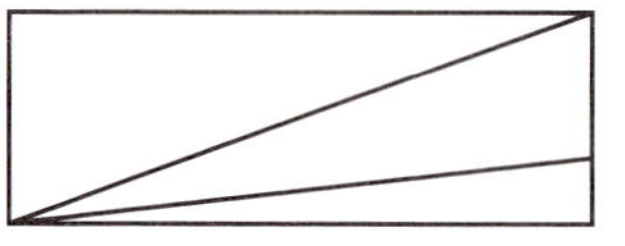
_____ parts — yes / no

5. 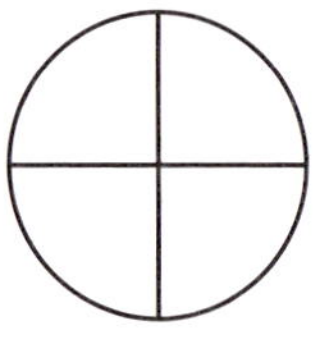
_____ parts — yes / no

6. 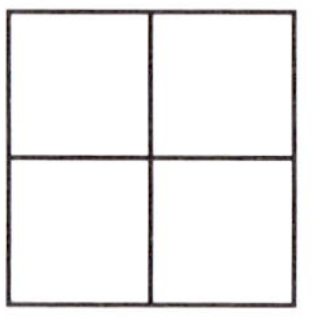
_____ parts — yes / no

7. 
_____ parts — yes / no

8. 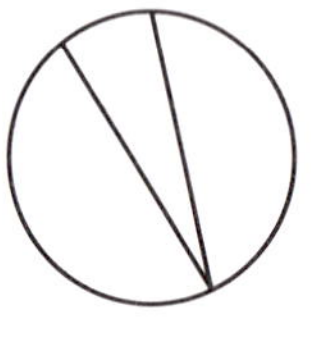
_____ parts — yes / no

Problem Solving ■ Visual Thinking

9. Susan has 2 apples. She wants to give each of her 8 friends an equal piece. Into how many pieces should she cut each apple?

_____ equal pieces

HOME ACTIVITY • With your child, fold paper to show equal parts. Ask your child to tell whether the parts are equal and then name the number of equal parts. Emphasize that the parts must be exactly the same size.

Name ______________________________

Unit Fractions

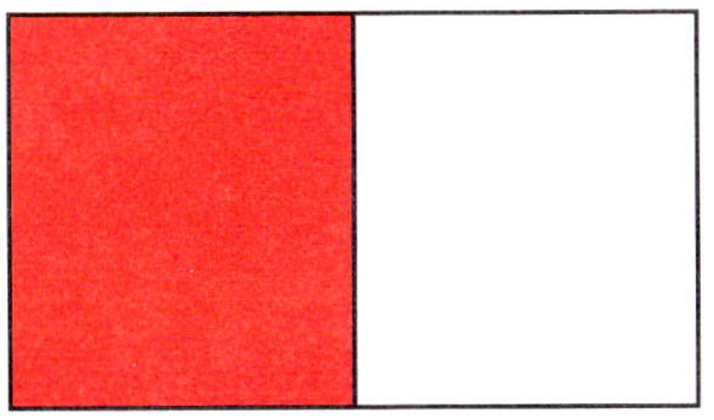

1 of 2 equal parts.
One-half is red.

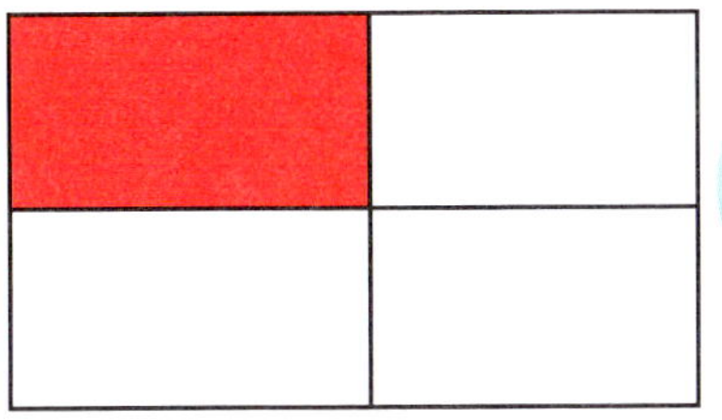

1 of 4 equal parts.
One-fourth is red.

$\frac{1}{2}$ 1 red part / 2 equal parts

$\frac{1}{4}$ 1 red part / 4 equal parts

The top number tells how many parts you are talking about.
The bottom number tells how many equal parts are in the whole.

Color one part red.
Circle the fraction for the red part.

1. 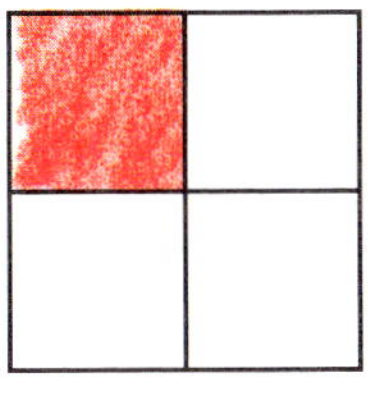

$\frac{1}{2}$ $\frac{1}{4}$ $\frac{1}{6}$

2. 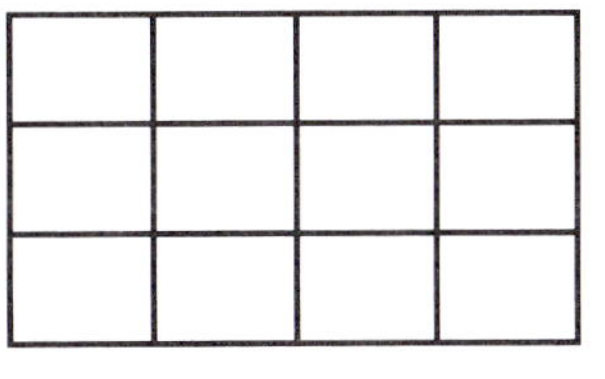

$\frac{1}{3}$ $\frac{1}{9}$ $\frac{1}{12}$

3. 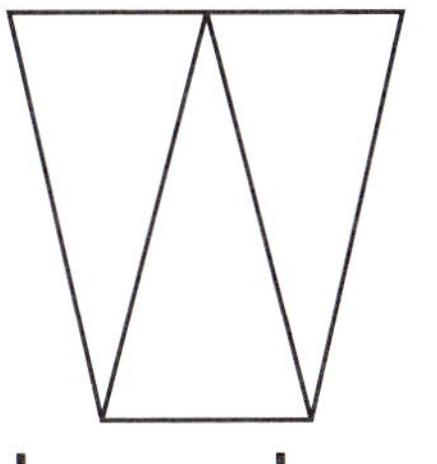

$\frac{1}{3}$ $\frac{1}{4}$ $\frac{1}{5}$

4. 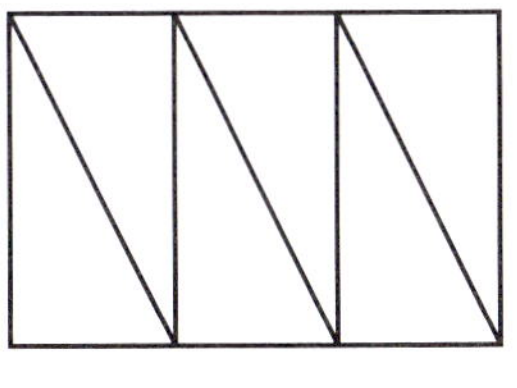

$\frac{1}{3}$ $\frac{1}{6}$ $\frac{1}{7}$

5. 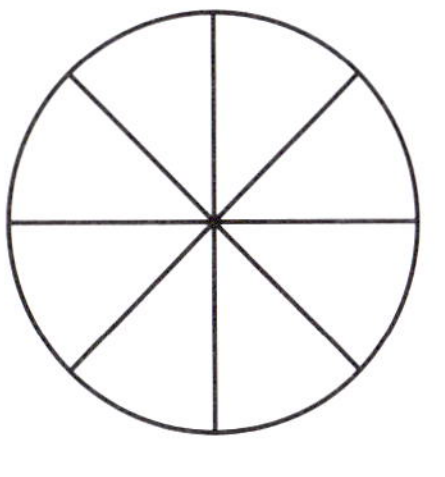

$\frac{1}{4}$ $\frac{1}{8}$ $\frac{1}{10}$

6. 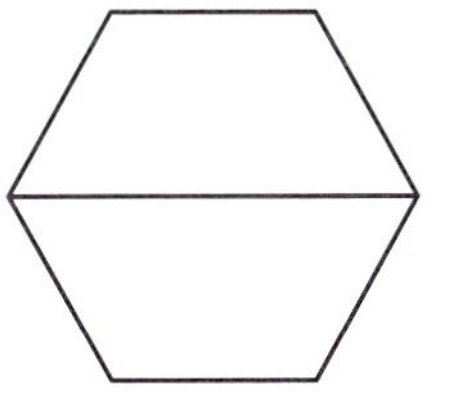

$\frac{1}{2}$ $\frac{1}{3}$ $\frac{1}{4}$

Talk About It ■ Reasoning

Larinda has $\frac{1}{2}$ of a red apple. Sarah has $\frac{1}{2}$ of a green apple.
Larinda says she has more than Sarah.
Could this be true? Explain.

Practice

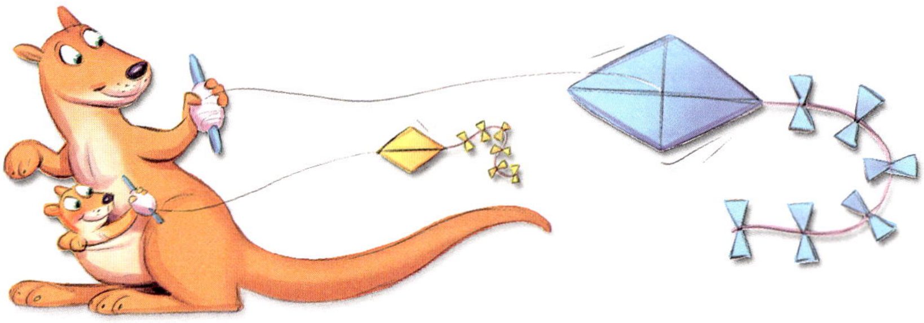

Color one part red.
Write the fraction for the red part.

1

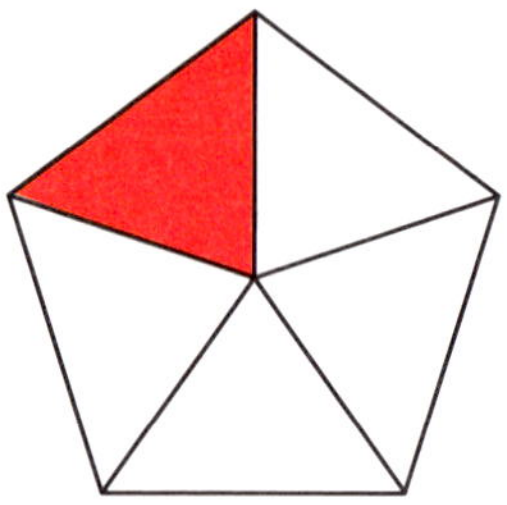

$\frac{1}{5}$

2

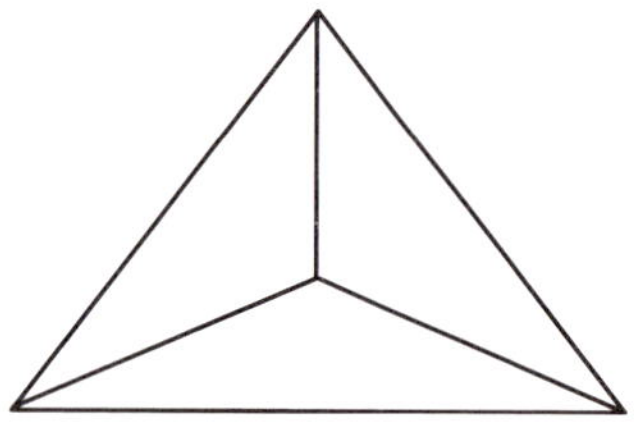

_____

3

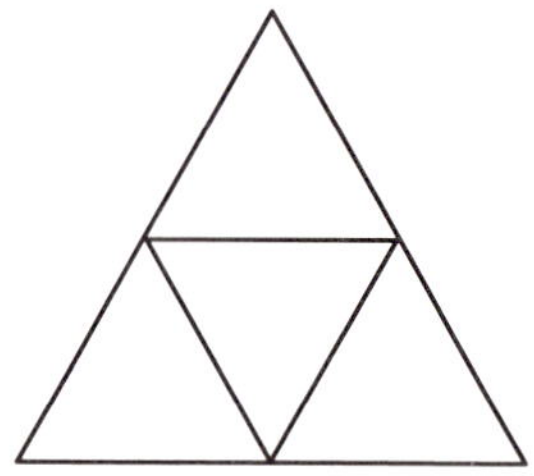

_____

4

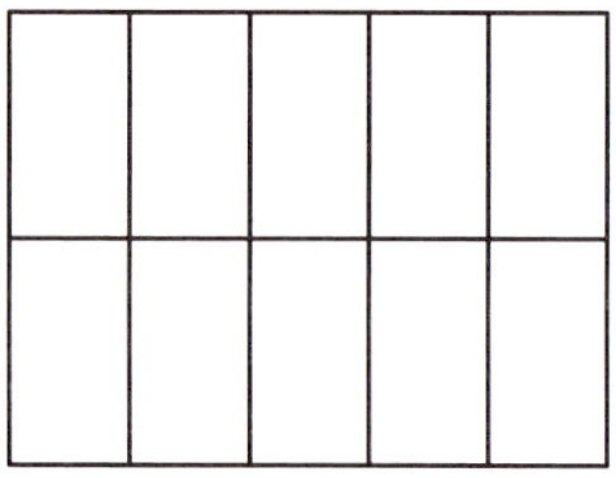

_____

5

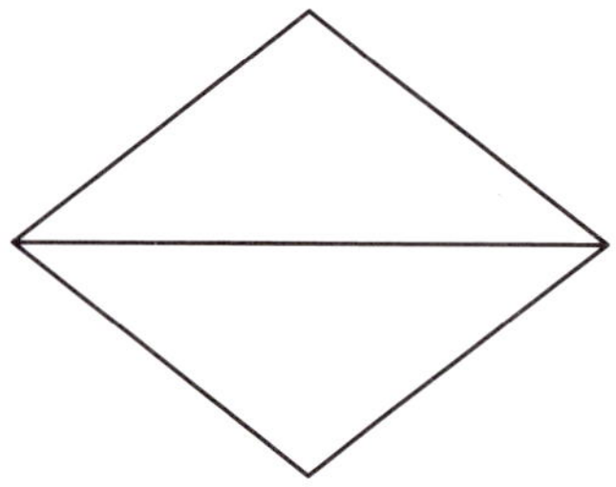

_____

6

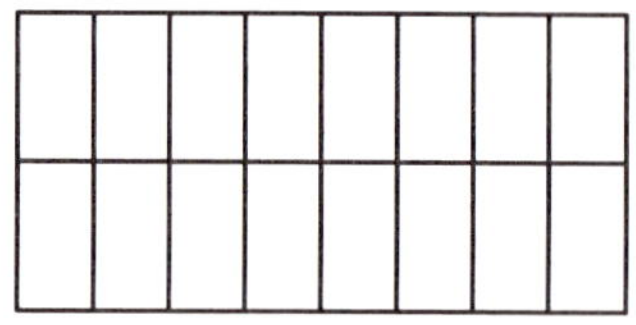

_____

7

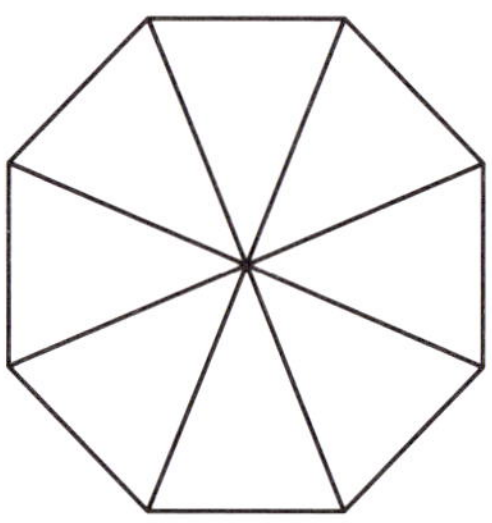

_____

8

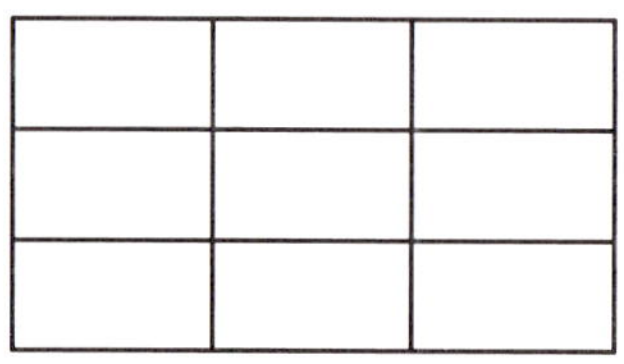

_____

9

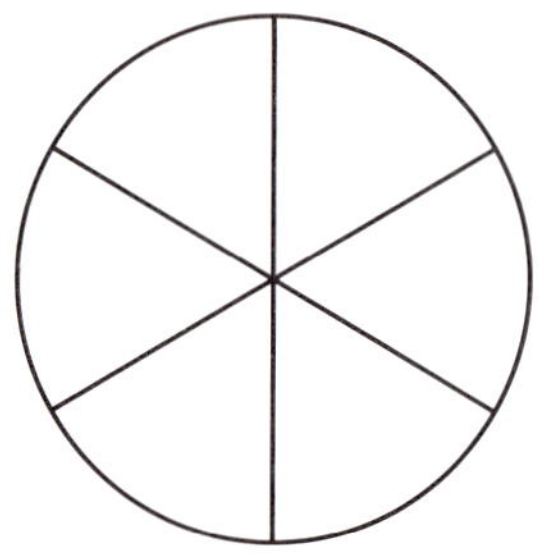

_____

Problem Solving ■ Visual Thinking

Circle the correct picture.

10 Which pizza has $\frac{1}{10}$ missing?

HOME ACTIVITY • With your child, draw pictures of shapes and divide them into equal parts. Ask your child to color one part and tell you the fraction.

Name ______________________________

Other Fractions

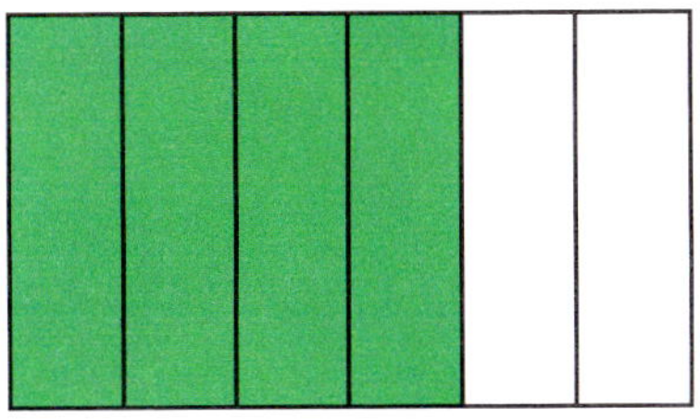

4 of 6 equal parts.
Four-sixths is green.

$\frac{4}{6}$ 4 green parts
6 equal parts

3 of 4 equal parts.
Three-fourths is green.

$\frac{3}{4}$ 3 green parts
4 equal parts

Color to show the fraction.

1. $\frac{3}{4}$

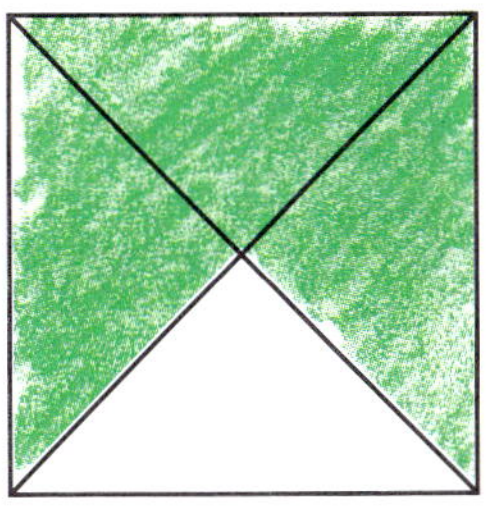

2. $\frac{7}{8}$

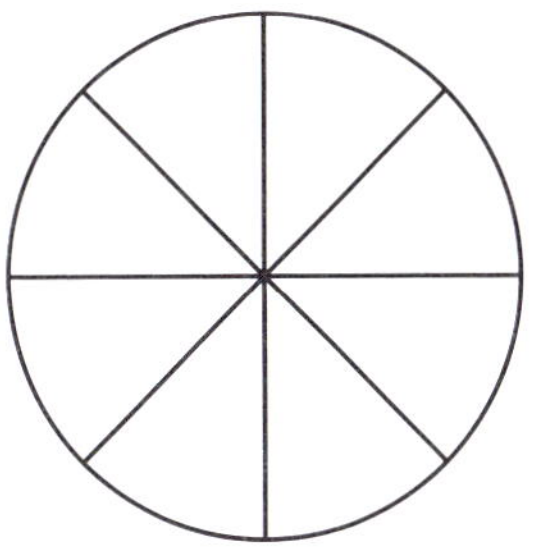

3. $\frac{4}{5}$

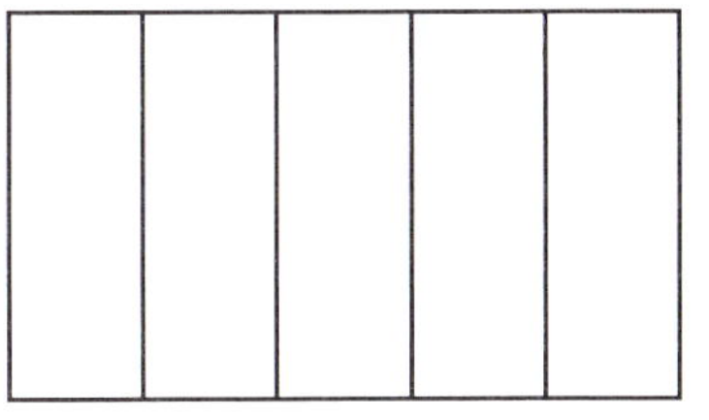

4. $\frac{4}{6}$

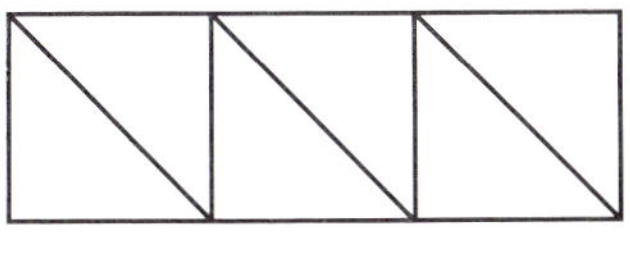

5. $\frac{2}{3}$

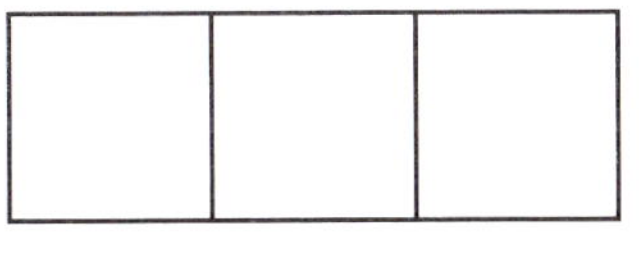

6. $\frac{6}{10}$

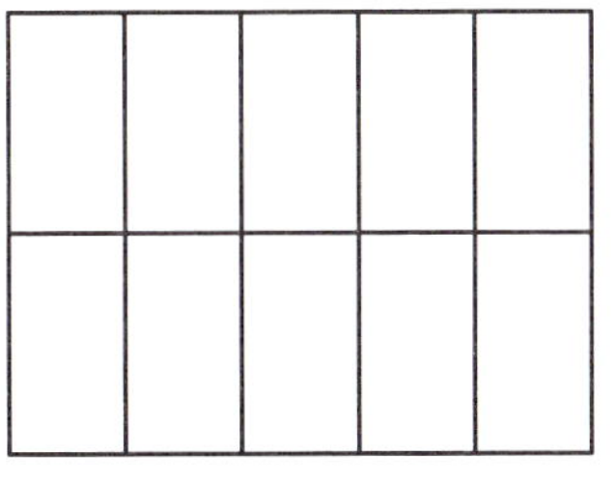

Talk About It ■ Reasoning

Look at problems 4 and 5. Would you rather have $\frac{4}{6}$ or $\frac{2}{3}$ of something? Explain.

Practice

Write the fraction for the green part.

1

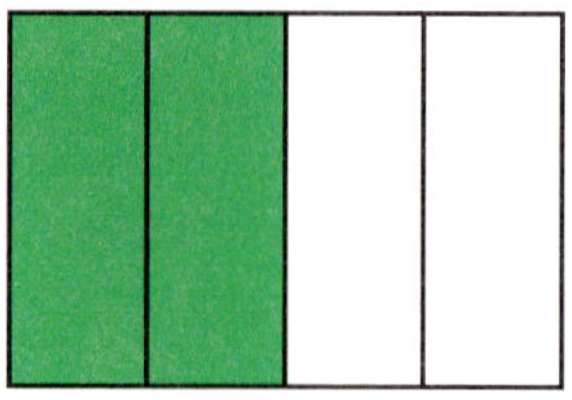

$\frac{2}{4}$

2

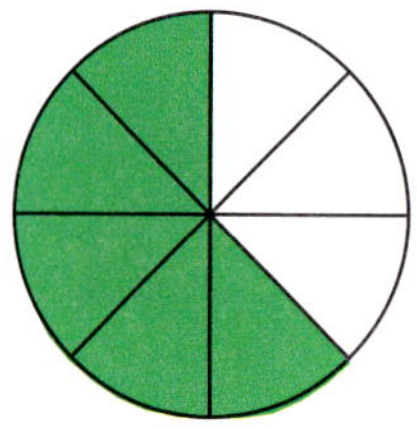

_____

3

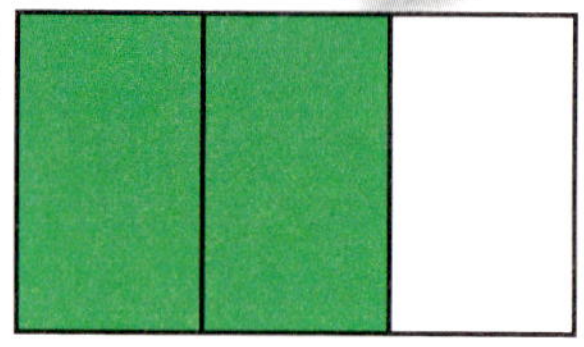

_____

4

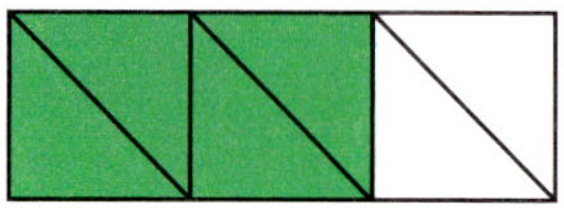

_____

5

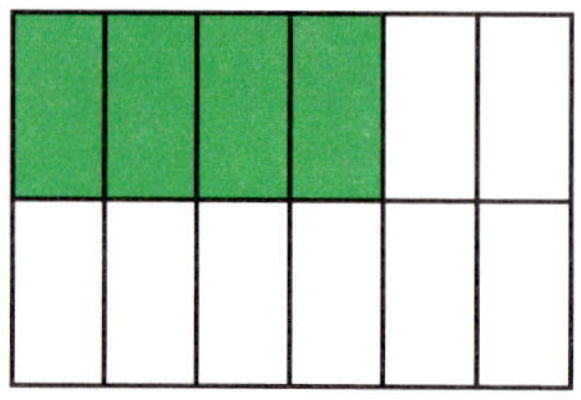

_____

6

_____

7

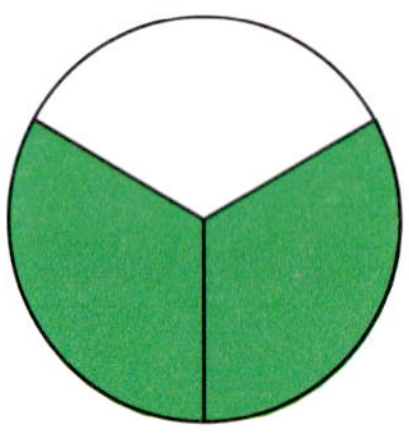

_____

8

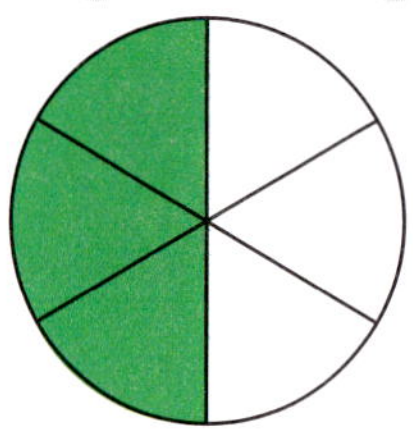

_____

9

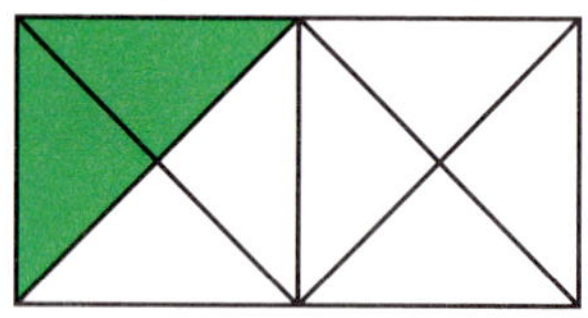

_____

Mixed Review

10 Write the time.

___ : ___

11 Write the amount.

_____ ¢

HOME ACTIVITY • Invite your child to divide food items into thirds, fourths, and sixths and tell you the fraction for one part and more than one part.

Name ______________________________

UNDERSTAND › PLAN › SOLVE › CHECK

Problem Solving
Make a Model

Which fraction is greater, $\frac{1}{3}$ or $\frac{1}{5}$?

UNDERSTAND

What do you want to find out?

PLAN

You can make a model to solve the problem.

SOLVE

$\frac{1}{5}$	$\frac{1}{5}$	$\frac{1}{5}$	$\frac{1}{5}$	$\frac{1}{5}$

$\frac{1}{3}$	$\frac{1}{3}$	$\frac{1}{3}$

$\frac{1}{3}$ is greater than $\frac{1}{5}$.

CHECK

Does your answer make sense? Explain.

Use fraction bars. Color one part of each whole. Circle the fraction that is greater.

1

$\frac{1}{2}$	$\frac{1}{2}$

$\frac{1}{4}$	$\frac{1}{4}$	$\frac{1}{4}$	$\frac{1}{4}$

($\frac{1}{2}$) $\frac{1}{4}$

2

$\frac{1}{10}$	$\frac{1}{10}$	$\frac{1}{10}$	$\frac{1}{10}$	$\frac{1}{10}$	$\frac{1}{10}$	$\frac{1}{10}$	$\frac{1}{10}$	$\frac{1}{10}$	$\frac{1}{10}$

$\frac{1}{6}$	$\frac{1}{6}$	$\frac{1}{6}$	$\frac{1}{6}$	$\frac{1}{6}$	$\frac{1}{6}$

$\frac{1}{10}$ $\frac{1}{6}$

Practice

Use fraction bars.
Color one part of each whole.
Circle the fraction that is less.

1

$\frac{1}{3}$	$\frac{1}{3}$	$\frac{1}{3}$

$\frac{1}{4}$	$\frac{1}{4}$	$\frac{1}{4}$	$\frac{1}{4}$

$\frac{1}{3}$ $\quad$ $\frac{1}{4}$

2

$\frac{1}{12}$	$\frac{1}{12}$	$\frac{1}{12}$	$\frac{1}{12}$	$\frac{1}{12}$	$\frac{1}{12}$	$\frac{1}{12}$	$\frac{1}{12}$	$\frac{1}{12}$	$\frac{1}{12}$	$\frac{1}{12}$	$\frac{1}{12}$

$\frac{1}{6}$	$\frac{1}{6}$	$\frac{1}{6}$	$\frac{1}{6}$	$\frac{1}{6}$	$\frac{1}{6}$

$\frac{1}{12}$ $\quad$ $\frac{1}{6}$

3

$\frac{1}{6}$	$\frac{1}{6}$	$\frac{1}{6}$	$\frac{1}{6}$	$\frac{1}{6}$	$\frac{1}{6}$

$\frac{1}{8}$	$\frac{1}{8}$	$\frac{1}{8}$	$\frac{1}{8}$	$\frac{1}{8}$	$\frac{1}{8}$	$\frac{1}{8}$	$\frac{1}{8}$

$\frac{1}{6}$ $\quad$ $\frac{1}{8}$

4

$\frac{1}{12}$	$\frac{1}{12}$	$\frac{1}{12}$	$\frac{1}{12}$	$\frac{1}{12}$	$\frac{1}{12}$	$\frac{1}{12}$	$\frac{1}{12}$	$\frac{1}{12}$	$\frac{1}{12}$	$\frac{1}{12}$	$\frac{1}{12}$

$\frac{1}{10}$	$\frac{1}{10}$	$\frac{1}{10}$	$\frac{1}{10}$	$\frac{1}{10}$	$\frac{1}{10}$	$\frac{1}{10}$	$\frac{1}{10}$	$\frac{1}{10}$	$\frac{1}{10}$

$\frac{1}{12}$ $\quad$ $\frac{1}{10}$

Problem Solving ■ Reasoning

Circle true or false.
Explain your thinking.

5

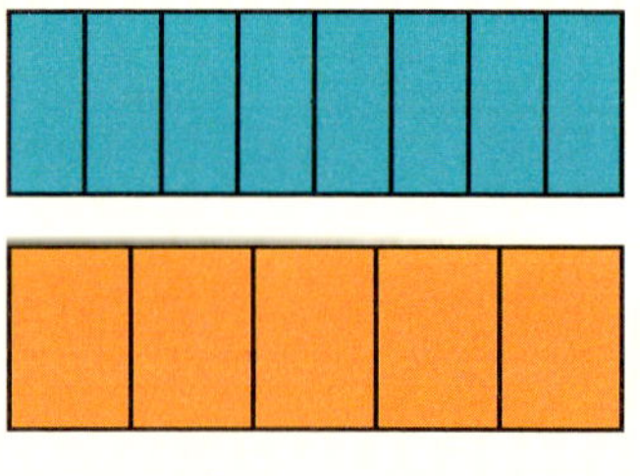

$\frac{1}{8} > \frac{1}{5}$

true $\quad$ false

6

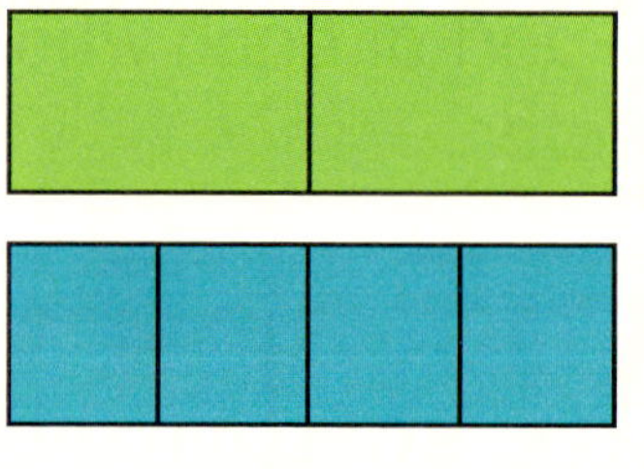

$\frac{1}{2} = \frac{2}{4}$

true $\quad$ false

7

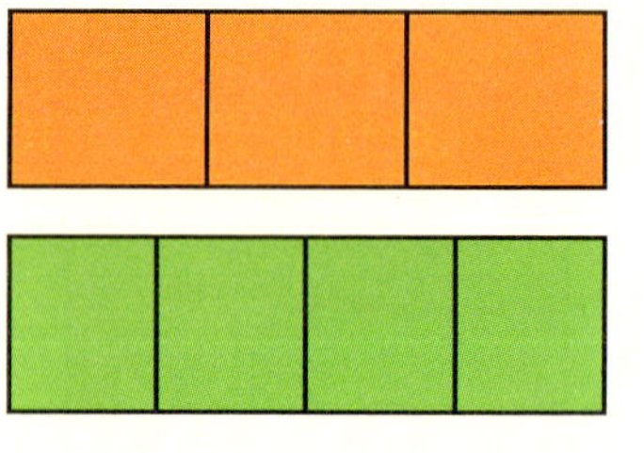

$\frac{1}{3} > \frac{1}{4}$

true $\quad$ false

HOME ACTIVITY • Cut the same food (for example, a slice of bread) into different numbers of equal parts. Ask your child to name each fractional part and tell which part is greater and which is less.

Name ____________________

Fractions Equal to 1

Each part is $\frac{1}{4}$ of the whole.

What is the fraction for the whole?

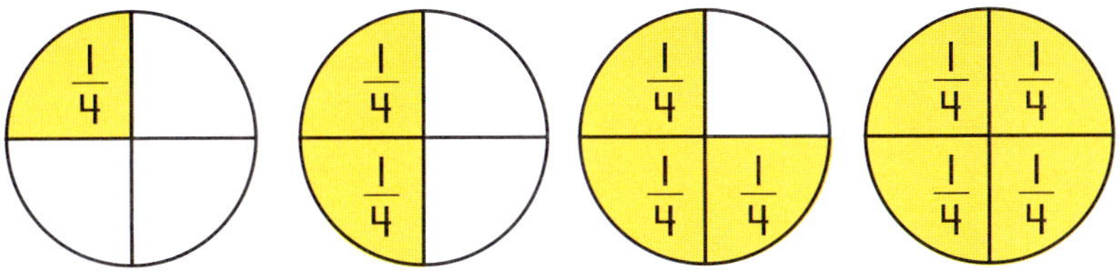

Count.

$\frac{1}{4}$ $\frac{2}{4}$ $\frac{3}{4}$ $\frac{4}{4}$

$\frac{4}{4}$ = 1 whole

The fraction for the whole always equals one.

Count the parts. Write each fraction.
Write the fraction for the whole.

1

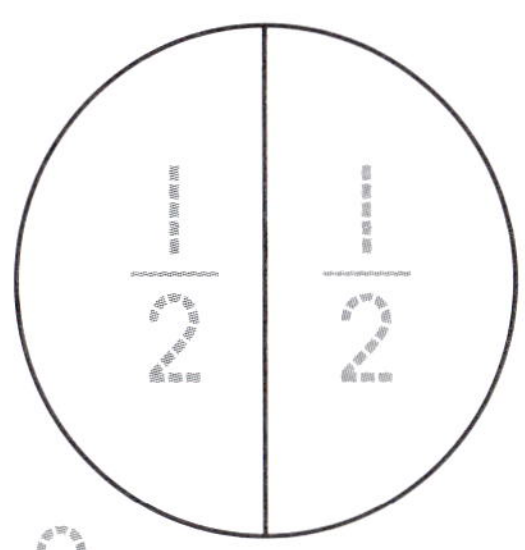

$\frac{2}{2}$ = 1 whole

2

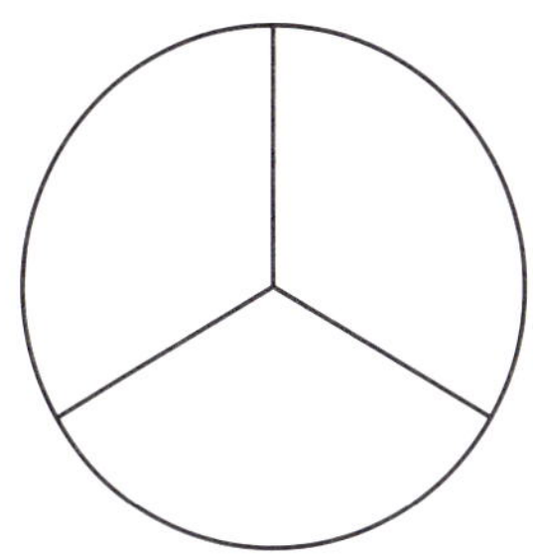

_______ = 1 whole

3

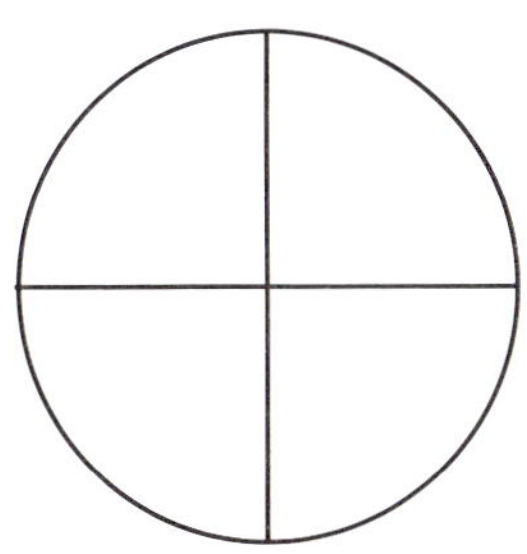

_______ = 1 whole

4

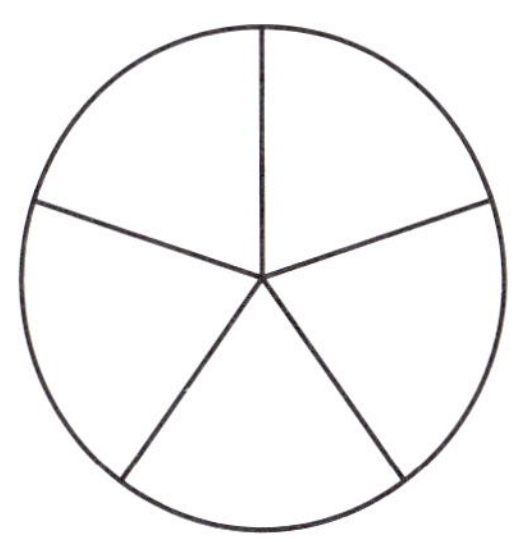

_______ = 1 whole

Talk About It ▪ Reasoning

If $\frac{2}{2}$ equals 1 whole, what does $\frac{4}{2}$ equal?

Practice

Count the parts. Write each fraction. Write the fraction for the whole.

1

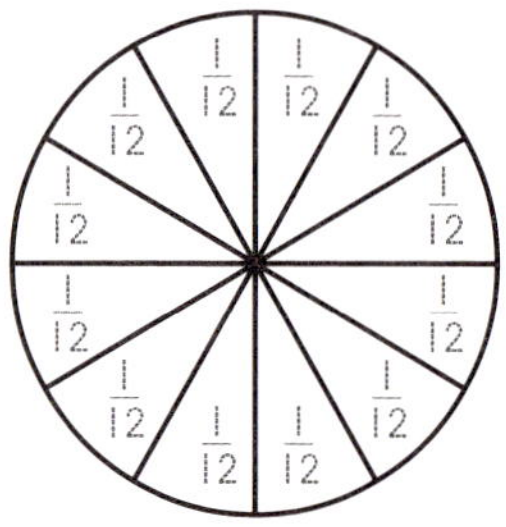

$\frac{12}{12}$ = 1 whole

2

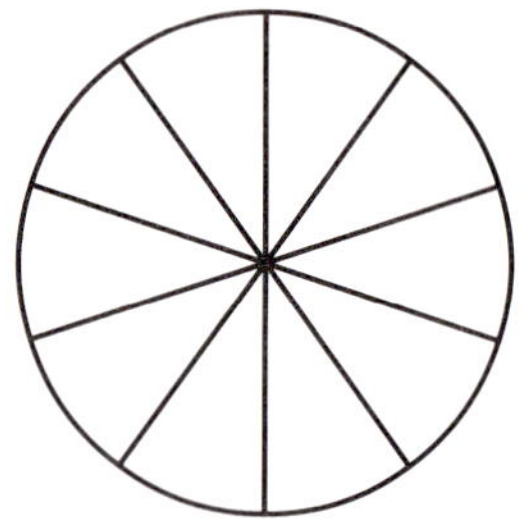

_______ = 1 whole

3

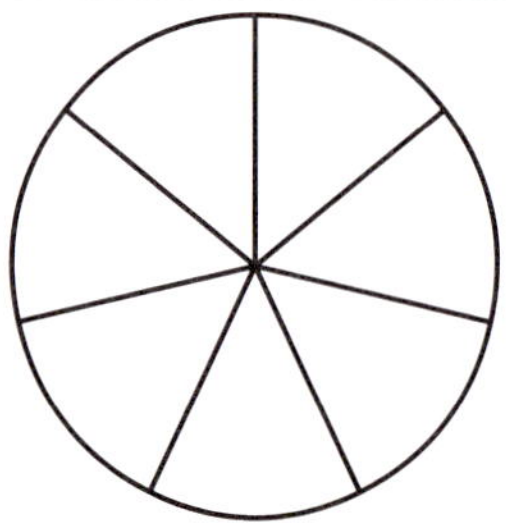

_______ = 1 whole

4

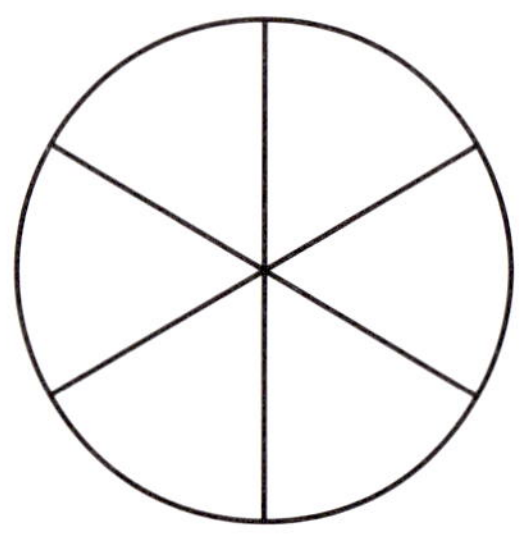

_______ = 1 whole

5

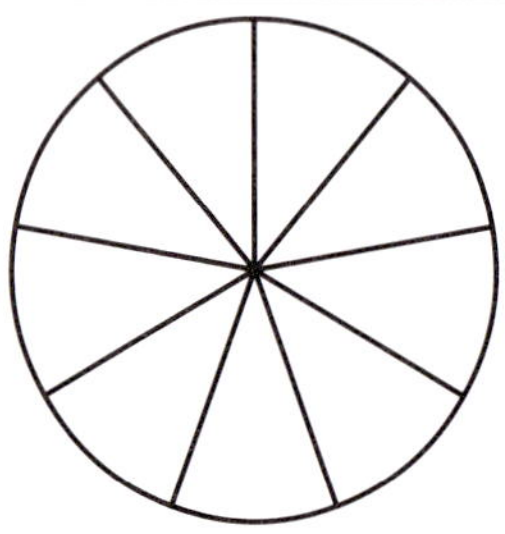

_______ = 1 whole

6

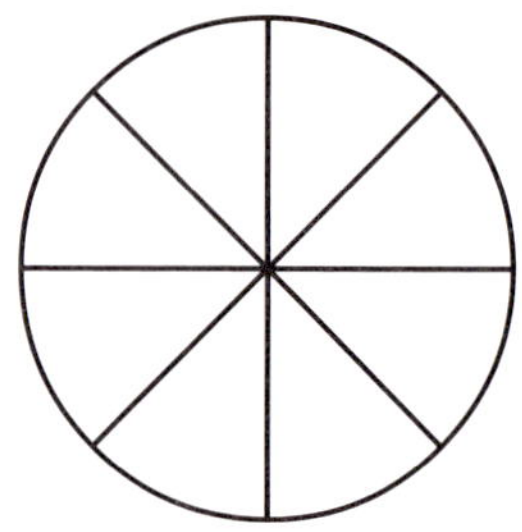

_______ = 1 whole

Problem Solving ■ Application

Show how to solve this problem.

7 There are 12 children at a party. Each child has $\frac{1}{6}$ of a pizza. How many whole pizzas will the children eat? _____ pizzas

HOME ACTIVITY • After you cut a sandwich or a pizza, ask your child to name the fraction for the whole.

Name ______________________________

Review/Test
Chapter 23

CHECK ■ Concepts and Skills

Write the number of parts.
Are the parts equal? Circle yes or no.

1

yes

no

______ parts

2

yes

no

______ parts

Color one part red.
Write the fraction for the red part.

3

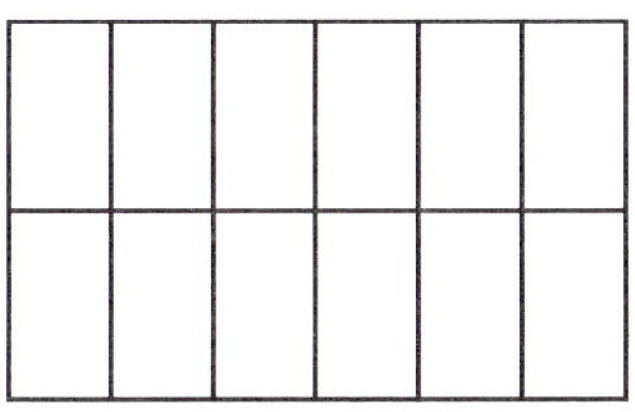

______

Write the fraction for the green part.

4

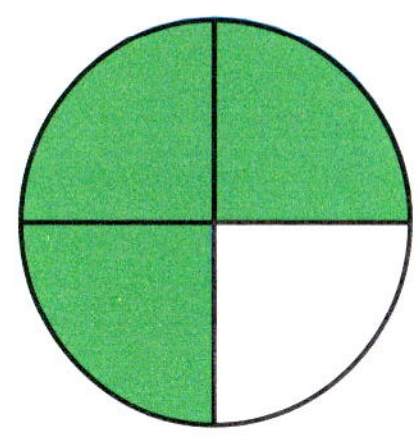

______

Count the parts. Write each fraction.
Write the fraction for the whole.

5

______ = 1 whole

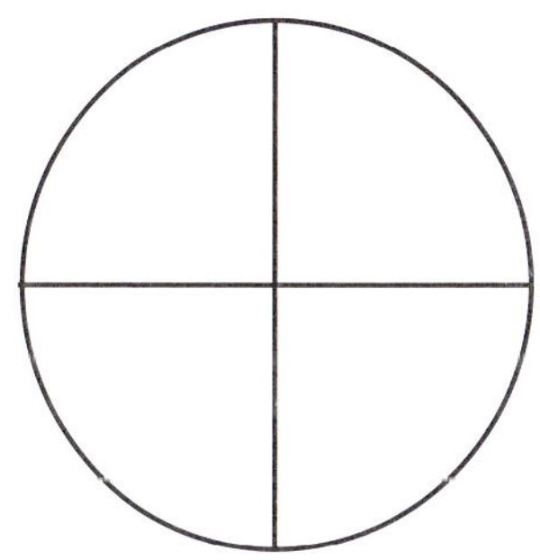

CHECK ■ Problem Solving

Use fraction bars. Color one part of each whole.
Circle the fraction that is greater.

6

$\frac{1}{6}$	$\frac{1}{6}$	$\frac{1}{6}$	$\frac{1}{6}$	$\frac{1}{6}$	$\frac{1}{6}$

$\frac{1}{4}$	$\frac{1}{4}$	$\frac{1}{4}$	$\frac{1}{4}$

$\frac{1}{4}$ $\frac{1}{6}$

7

$\frac{1}{8}$	$\frac{1}{8}$	$\frac{1}{8}$	$\frac{1}{8}$	$\frac{1}{8}$	$\frac{1}{8}$	$\frac{1}{8}$	$\frac{1}{8}$

$\frac{1}{10}$	$\frac{1}{10}$	$\frac{1}{10}$	$\frac{1}{10}$	$\frac{1}{10}$	$\frac{1}{10}$	$\frac{1}{10}$	$\frac{1}{10}$	$\frac{1}{10}$	$\frac{1}{10}$

$\frac{1}{8}$ $\frac{1}{10}$

Name ______________________

Standardized Test Prep
Chapters 1–23

Choose the best answer for questions 1–4.

1. Which picture shows 3 equal parts?

○ ○ ○ ○

2. Which fraction tells what part is shaded?

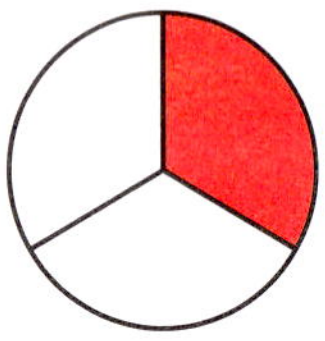

○ $\frac{1}{2}$ ○ $\frac{1}{3}$ ○ $\frac{1}{4}$ ○ $\frac{1}{5}$

3. Which fraction tells what part is shaded?

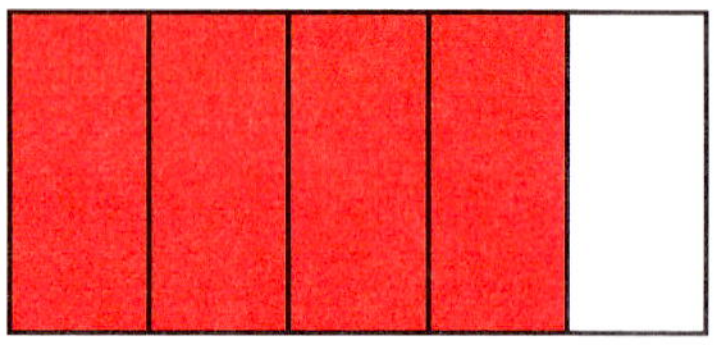

○ $\frac{1}{5}$ ○ $\frac{1}{4}$ ○ $\frac{5}{4}$ ○ $\frac{4}{5}$

4. Which fraction names the whole circle?

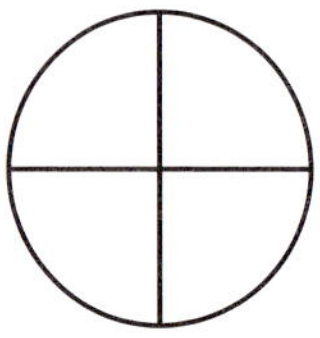

○ $\frac{1}{4}$ ○ $\frac{2}{4}$ ○ $\frac{3}{4}$ ○ $\frac{4}{4}$

Show What You Know

5. Draw a rectangle.
Draw 4 equal parts.

Color some parts blue.
What fraction is blue?

$\frac{\square}{\square}$ is blue.

Chapter 24 Parts of a Group

The girl picked 8 apples. What fraction tells the part of the group that is green?

SCHOOL HOME CONNECTION

Dear Family,

Today we started Chapter 24. We will look at fractions and learn ways to find equal parts of groups. Here is the math vocabulary and an activity for us to do together at home.

Love,

____

My Math Words

one-half
three-fourths

Vocabulary

one-half One of two equal parts.

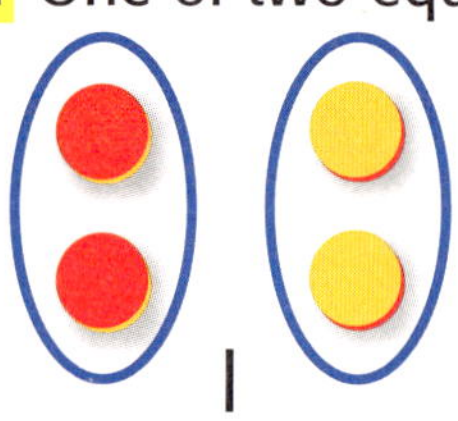

$\frac{1}{2}$

three-fourths Three of four equal parts.

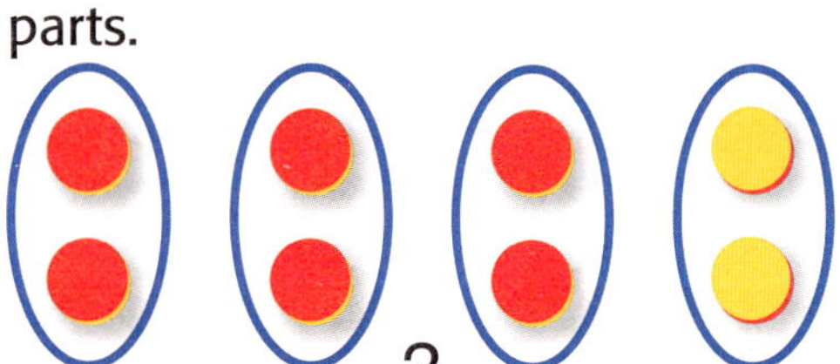

$\frac{3}{4}$

Visit ***The Learning Site*** **for additional ideas and activities.**
www.harcourtschool.com

ACTIVITY

Help your child learn about fractions at snack time. For example, you might spread 2 out of 6 crackers with peanut butter and the other 4 crackers with cheese. Have your child draw a picture and write the fraction for each part of the snack.

Books to Share

To read about fractions with your child, look for these books in your local library.

Eating Fractions,
by Bruce McMillan,
Scholastic, 1991.

Jump, Kangaroo, Jump,
by Stuart J. Murphy,
HarperCollins, 1999.

Name ______________________________

Explore Fractions

Use 🔴.
Write the fraction for the yellow part.

A fraction can name part of a group.

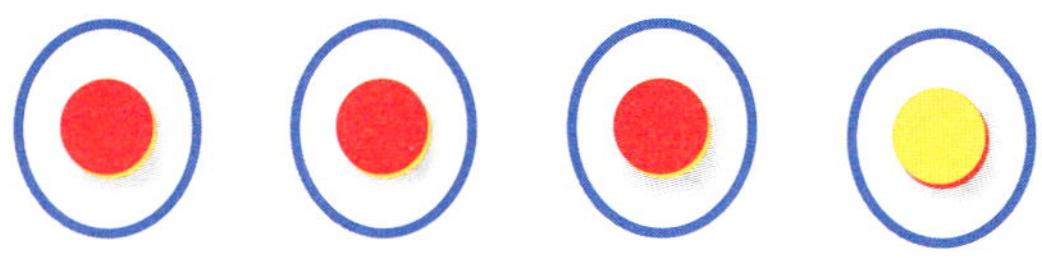

There are 4 equal parts.

The yellow part is $\frac{1}{4}$.

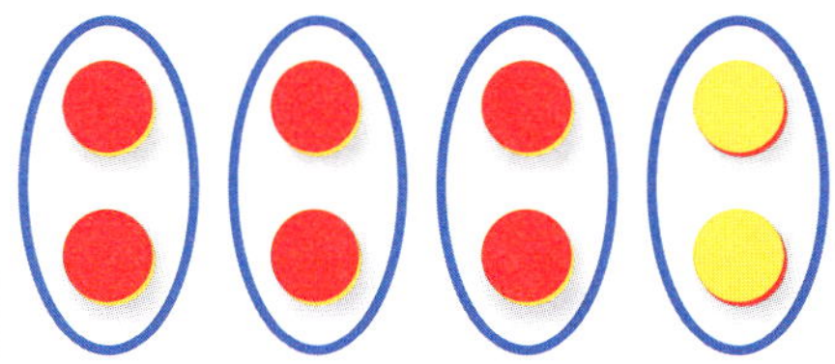

There are 4 equal parts.

The yellow part is $\frac{1}{4}$.

Use 🔴.
Write the fraction for the yellow part.

1 3 equal parts

$\frac{1}{3}$

2 2 equal parts

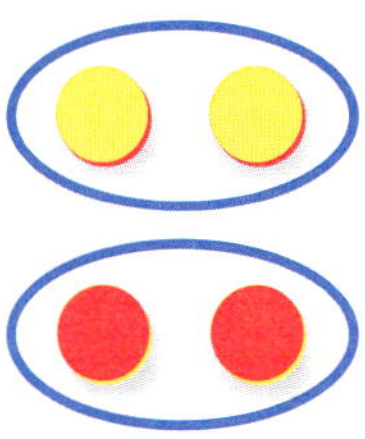

______

3 4 equal parts

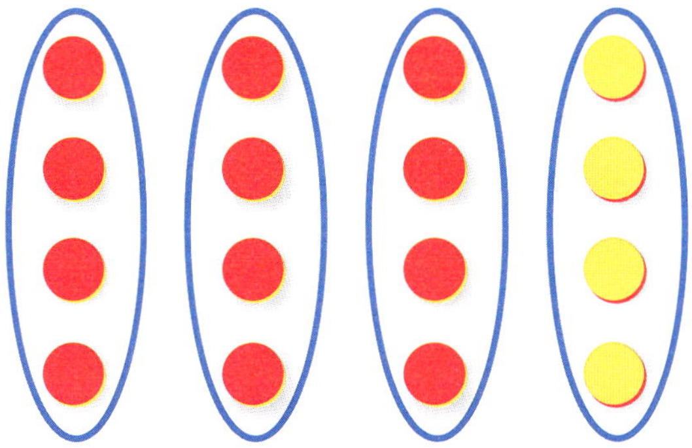

______

4 3 equal parts

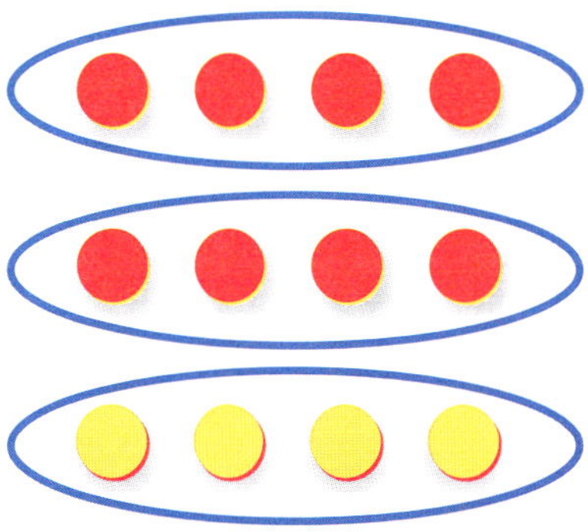

______

Talk About It • Reasoning

How can you tell if the parts of a group are equal?

Practice

Write the fraction for the yellow part.

1. 3 equal parts

$\frac{1}{3}$

2. 2 equal parts

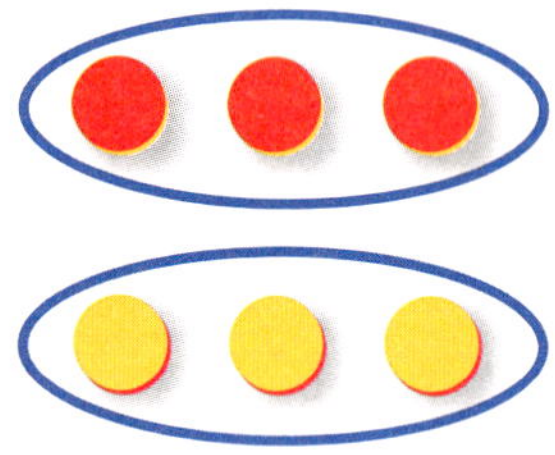

______

3. 2 equal parts

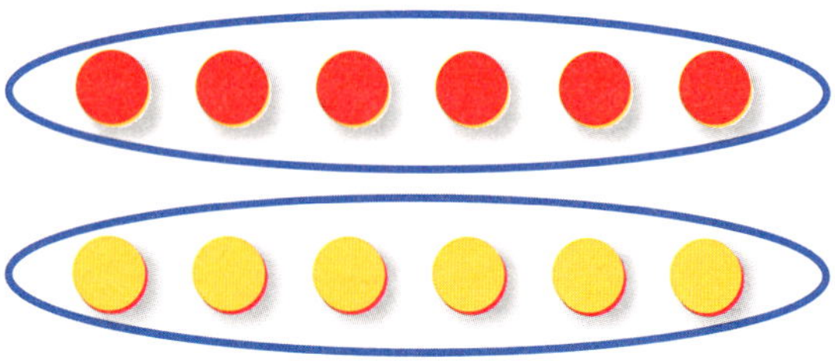

______

4. 4 equal parts

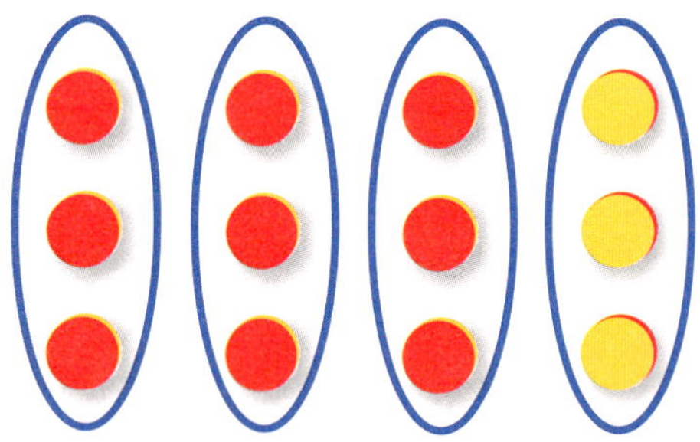

______

5. 3 equal parts

______

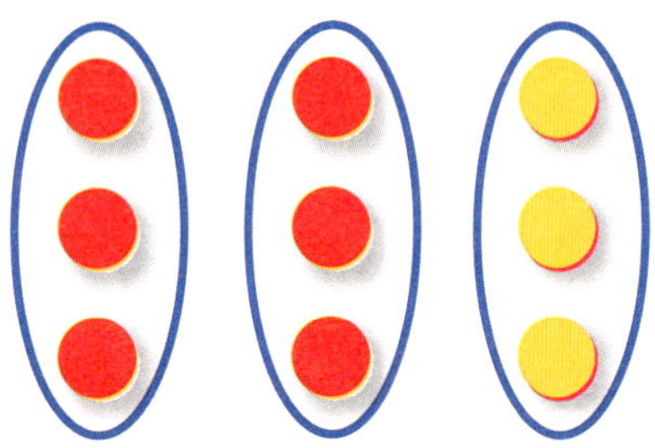

6. 2 equal parts

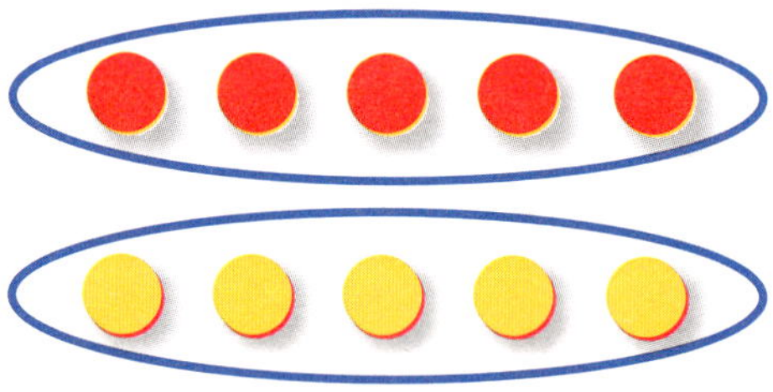

______

Problem Solving • Visual Thinking

Are the parts equal? Circle **yes** or **no**.

7. 

yes no

8. 

yes no

HOME ACTIVITY • With your child, use pennies to show groups with equal parts. Ask your child to tell whether the parts are equal and then name the number of equal parts.

Name ______________________________

Unit Fractions

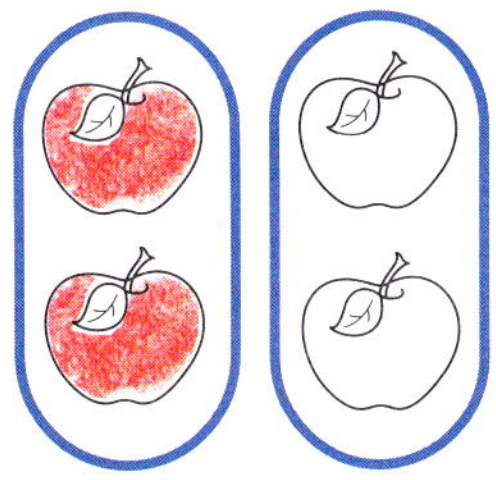

1 of 2 equal parts.
One-half is red.

$\frac{1}{2}$ 1 red part
2 equal parts

The top number tells how many parts you are talking about.

The bottom number tells how many equal parts are in the group.

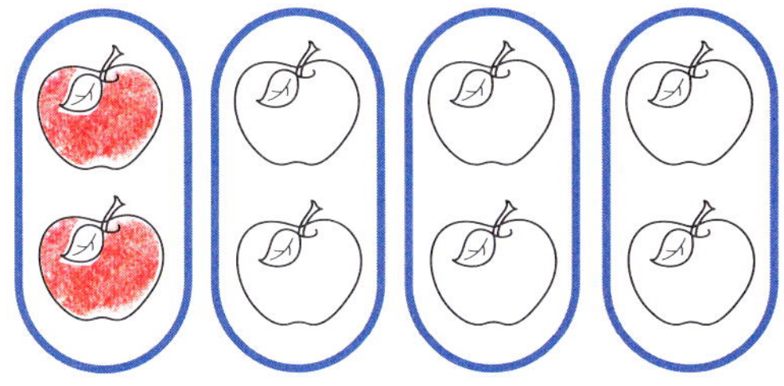

1 of 4 equal parts.
One-fourth is red.

$\frac{1}{4}$ 1 red part
4 equal parts

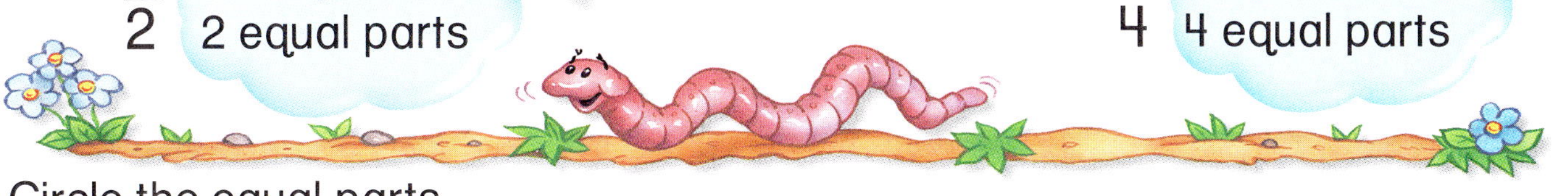

Circle the equal parts.
Color to show the fraction.

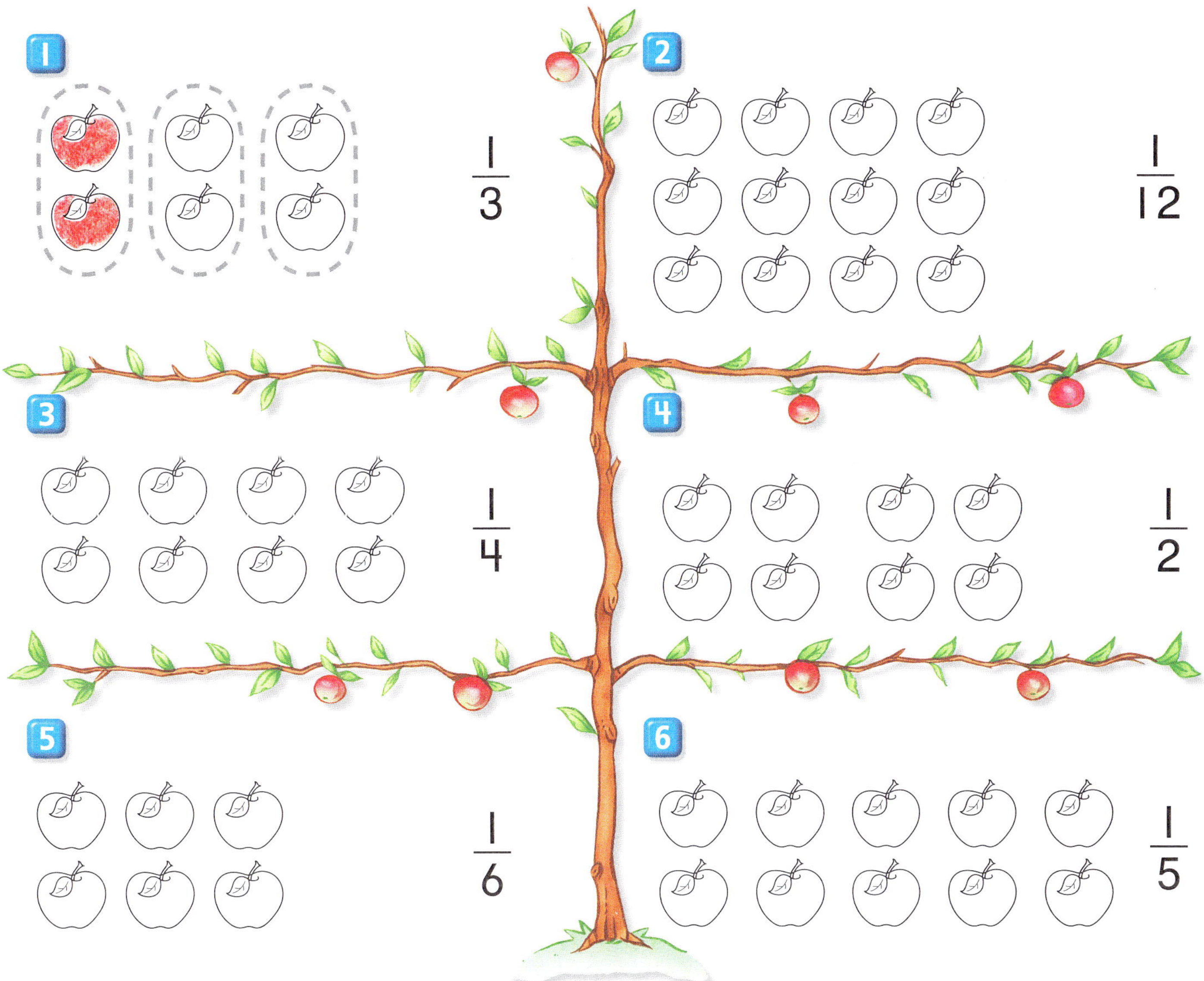

Talk About It ■ **Reasoning**

Look at problem 4. Circle apples to show more than 2 equal groups. What is the fraction? Explain.

Practice

Circle the equal parts.
Color to show the fraction.

1

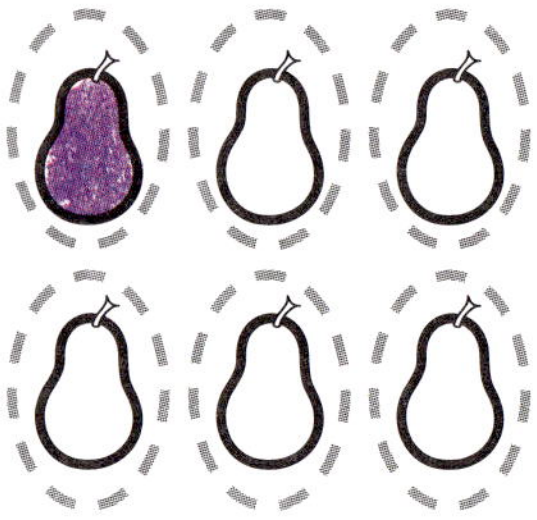

$\frac{1}{6}$

2

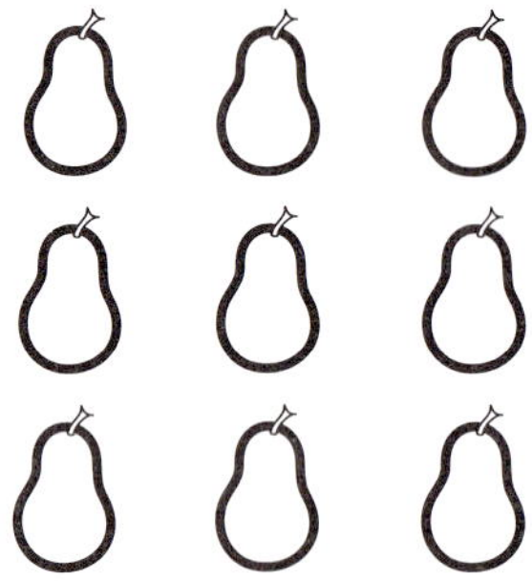

$\frac{1}{3}$

3

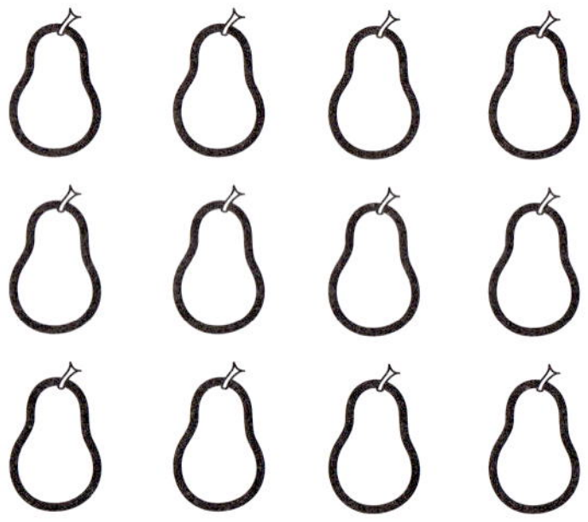

$\frac{1}{4}$

4

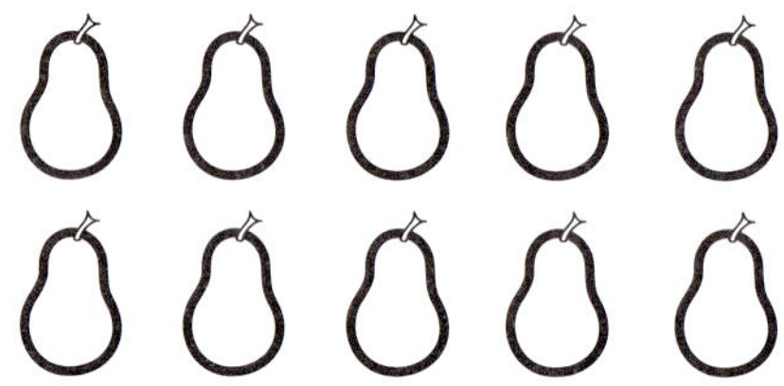

$\frac{1}{5}$

5

$\frac{1}{2}$

6

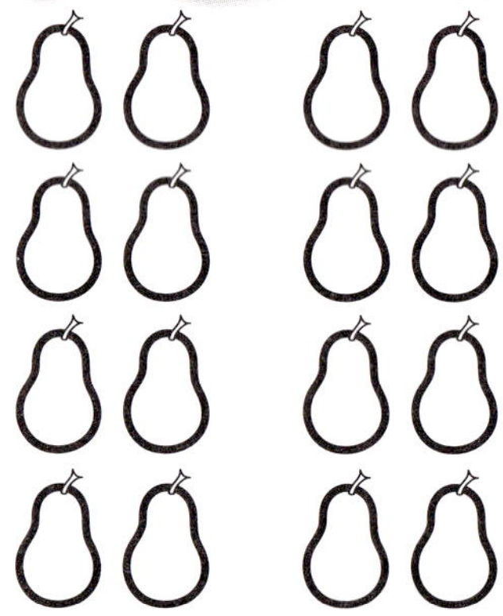

$\frac{1}{8}$

Mixed Review

Write how many sides and corners.

7

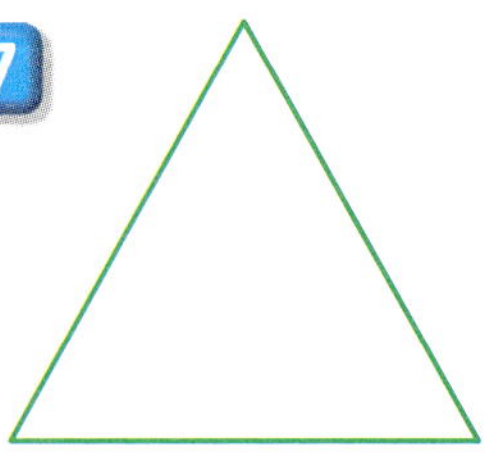

_______ sides

_______ corners

8

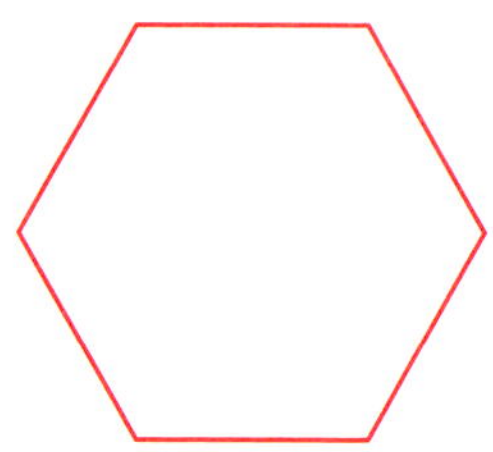

_______ sides

_______ corners

HOME ACTIVITY • Invite your child to divide a group of objects into halves, thirds, or fourths.

Name ______________________________

Other Fractions

2 of 3 equal parts.
Two-thirds are blue.

$\frac{2}{3}$ 2 blue parts / 3 equal parts

The top number tells how many parts you are talking about.
The bottom number tells how many equal parts are in the group.

3 of 4 equal parts.
Three-fourths are blue.

$\frac{3}{4}$ 3 blue parts / 4 equal parts

Write the fraction for the blue part.

1.  ______

2.  ______

3.  ______

4.  ______

5.  ______

6.  ______

7.  ______

8.  ______

9.  ______

Talk About It • Reasoning

Larry has 2 blue marbles and 2 red marbles.
What two fractions show how many parts of this group are blue?

Practice

Toss 3 ●.
Color these counters to show your toss.
Write the fraction for each color. Repeat.

1 $\frac{1}{3}$ red $\frac{2}{3}$ yellow

2 ______ red ______ yellow

3 ______ red ______ yellow

4 ______ red ______ yellow

5 ______ red ______ yellow

6 ______ red ______ yellow

Problem Solving ■ Application

Write a fraction to solve.

7 Dan has 3 oatmeal cookies and 3 raisin cookies. What fraction of the cookies are oatmeal?

______ oatmeal cookies

HOME ACTIVITY • With your child, use pennies to show groups with equal parts. Turn some of the pennies to show heads, and ask your child to tell what fraction of the group shows heads.

Name ______________________________

Compare Parts of a Group

Compare parts of a group. Look at > or <.
Circle true or false.

$\frac{1}{3}$

$\frac{2}{3}$

$\frac{1}{3} < \frac{2}{3}$

true (circled)   false

$\frac{1}{4}$

$\frac{2}{4}$

$\frac{2}{4} < \frac{1}{4}$

true   false (circled)

1

$\frac{2}{4}$

$\frac{3}{4}$

$\frac{2}{4} > \frac{3}{4}$

true   false

2

$\frac{1}{5}$

$\frac{4}{5}$

$\frac{1}{5} < \frac{4}{5}$

true   false

3

$\frac{4}{6}$

$\frac{3}{6}$

$\frac{4}{6} > \frac{3}{6}$

true   false

4

$\frac{2}{3}$

$\frac{3}{3}$

$\frac{2}{3} < \frac{3}{3}$

true   false

Talk About It ■ Reasoning

How do you know that $\frac{1}{3}$ of a group of 6 is less than $\frac{2}{3}$ of a group of 6?

Practice

Compare the red parts. Write > or <.

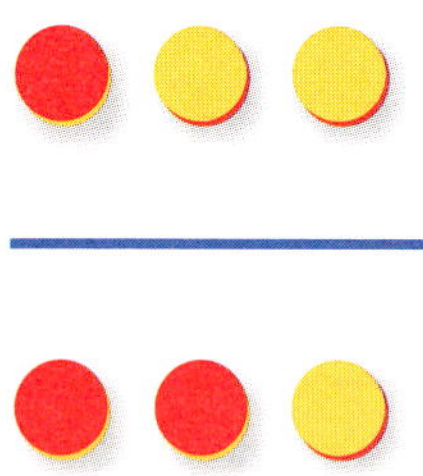

$\frac{1}{3}$

$\frac{2}{3}$

$\frac{1}{3}$ is less than $\frac{2}{3}$.

$\frac{1}{3} < \frac{2}{3}$

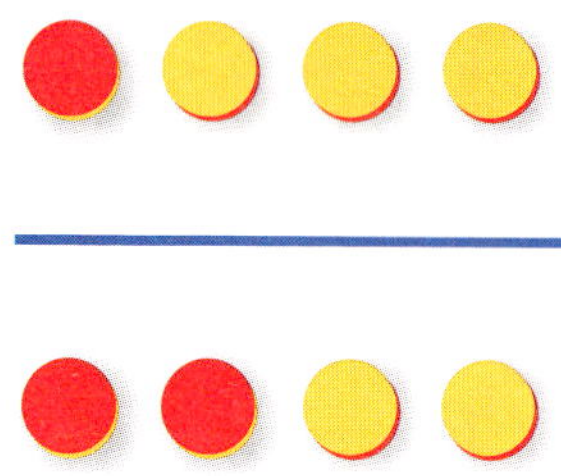

$\frac{1}{4}$

$\frac{2}{4}$

$\frac{2}{4}$ is greater than $\frac{1}{4}$.

$\frac{2}{4} > \frac{1}{4}$

Compare the red parts .
Write > or <.

1

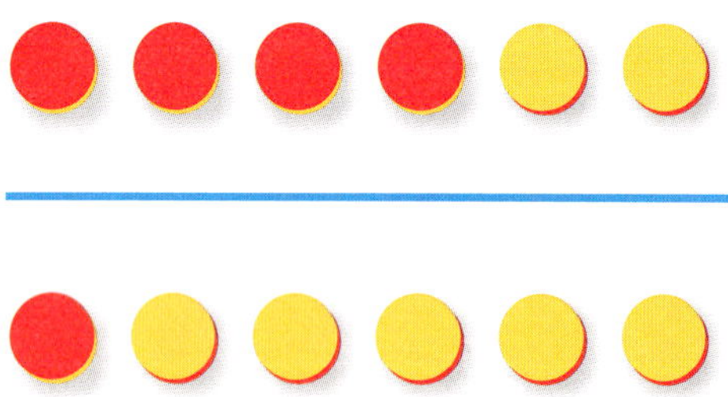

$\frac{4}{6}$

$\frac{1}{6}$

$\frac{4}{6} \bigcirc \frac{1}{6}$

2

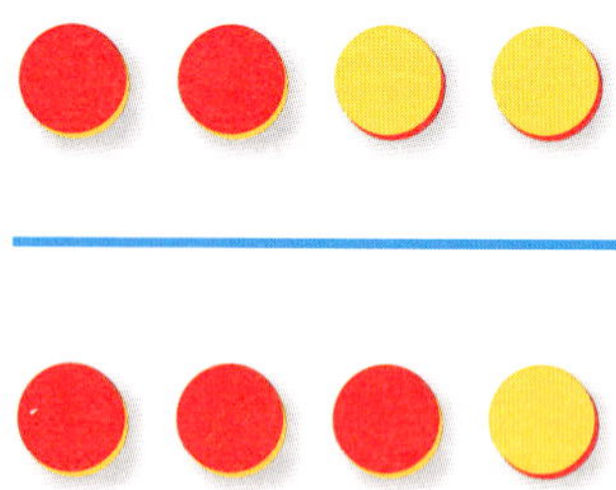

$\frac{2}{4}$

$\frac{3}{4}$

$\bigcirc$

Problem Solving ■ Reasoning

Circle true or false. Explain your thinking.

3

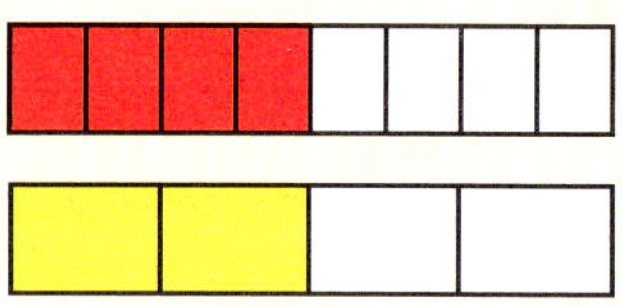

$\frac{4}{8} = \frac{2}{4}$

true false

4

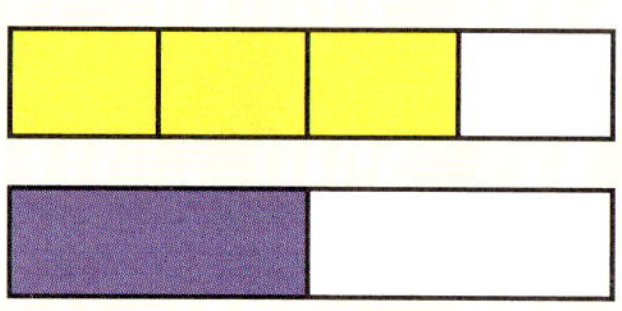

$\frac{3}{4} < \frac{1}{2}$

true false

5

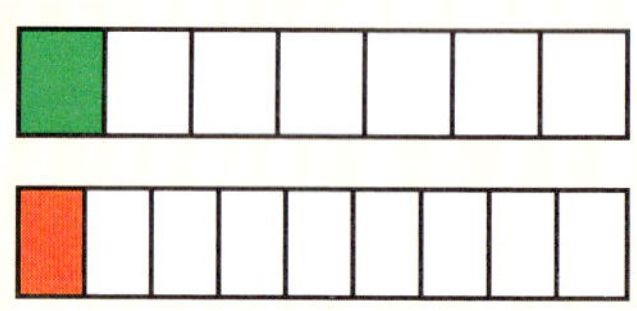

$\frac{1}{7} < \frac{1}{9}$

true false

HOME ACTIVITY • During mealtime, set out a group of 5 peas, chicken nuggets, or other foods. Eat 1 part and have your child eat 2 parts. Ask your child to name the fractional part each of you ate and tell who ate the greater part.

Name ______________________________

UNDERSTAND › PLAN › SOLVE › CHECK

Problem Solving
Make a Model

Cheryl ate $\frac{1}{3}$ of a small pizza.
Mike ate $\frac{1}{8}$ of the same size pizza.
Who ate more pizza?

UNDERSTAND

You need to find out who ate more pizza.

PLAN

Choose a way to solve the problem.

SOLVE

Make a model.

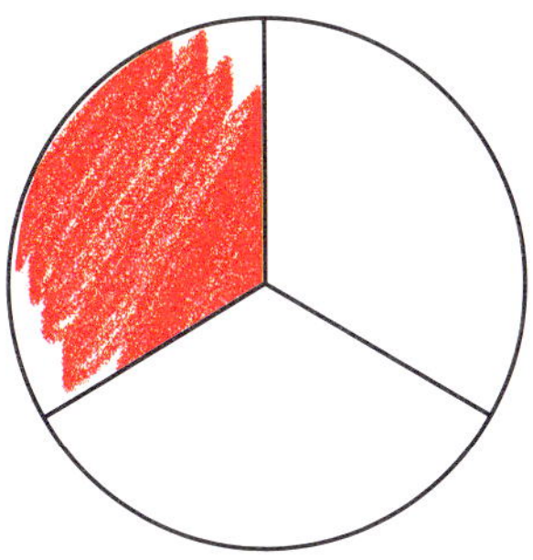

Cheryl's Pizza

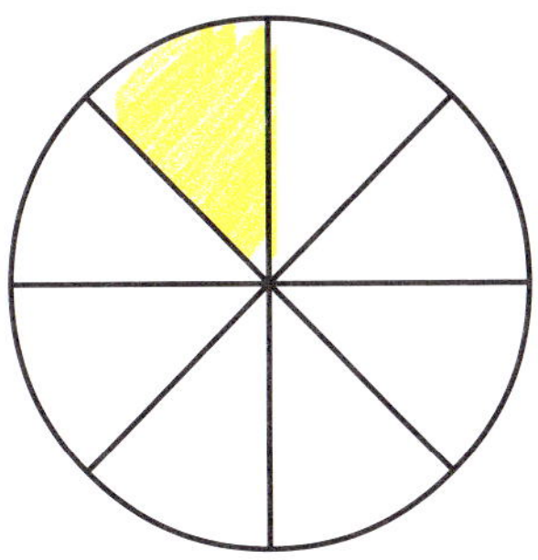

Mike's Pizza

CHECK

How did your model help you know who ate more pizza? Explain.

Make a model to solve these problems.

1. Caryn ate $\frac{1}{4}$ of a grapefruit.

   Beth ate $\frac{1}{2}$ of a grapefruit.

   Who ate more grapefruit? ________

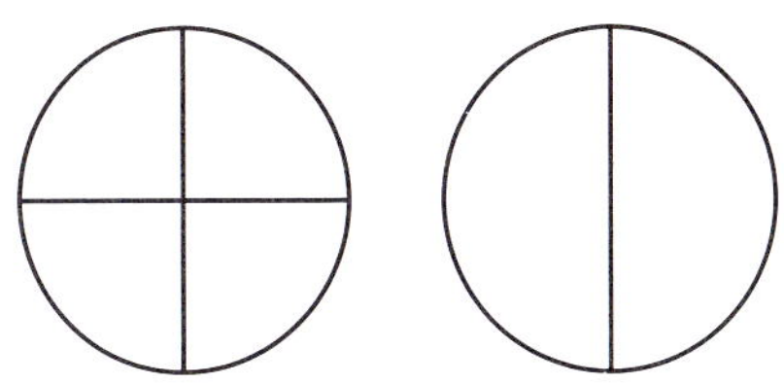

2. Kevin cut an apple into 6 equal pieces.
   Then he ate 2 pieces.
   What part did Kevin eat?

   ____

Practice

Use ●. Make and draw a model to solve.

1 Tim has 3 apples. $\frac{1}{3}$ of the apples are green.
$\frac{2}{3}$ of the apples are red.
Are there more red or green apples?

red

2 Frank has 4 marbles. 3 marbles are blue and 1 marble is red. What fraction of the marbles are blue?

______

3 Sasha has 6 oranges. She gives $\frac{2}{6}$ of the oranges to Roy. She keeps $\frac{4}{6}$ of them. Who has more oranges?

______

4 Toni has 2 corn muffins and 3 bran muffins. What fraction of the muffins are bran?

______

Math Journal

Write About It

Write a story about two friends sharing food.
Use fractions to tell how much each friend eats.

HOME ACTIVITY • Make up problems similar to the ones on this page. Have your child use objects to model and solve them.

Name ________________________

Review/Test
Chapter 24

CHECK ▪ Concepts and Skills

Write the fraction for the yellow part.

1. 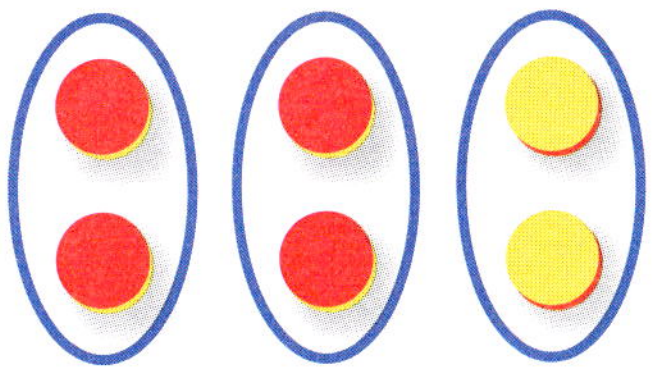

______

2. 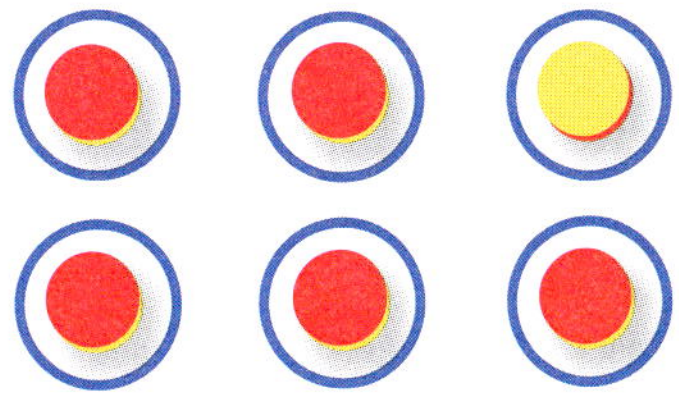

______

3. 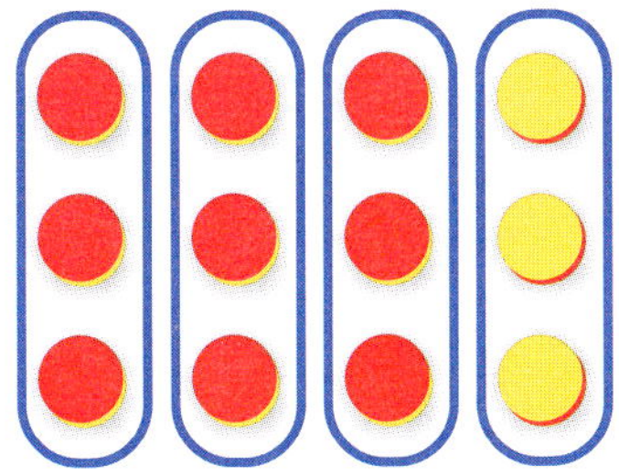

______

Write the fraction for the blue part.

4. 

______

5. 

______

6. 

______

Compare the blue parts. Look at > or <. Circle true or false.

7. 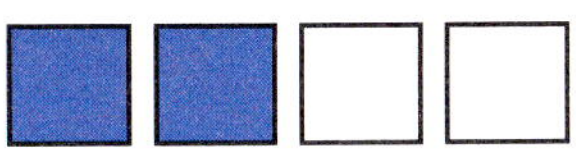 $\frac{2}{4}$

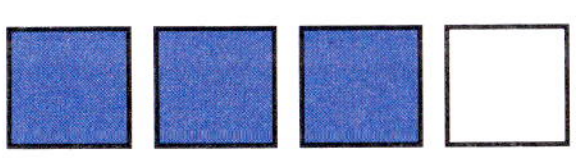 $\frac{3}{4}$

$\frac{2}{4} < \frac{3}{4}$

true false

8.  $\frac{4}{5}$

 $\frac{2}{5}$

$\frac{4}{5} < \frac{2}{5}$

true false

CHECK ▪ Problem Solving

Use 4 🟡. Make and draw a model to solve.

9. Art has 4 apples. $\frac{1}{4}$ of the apples are green. $\frac{3}{4}$ of the apples are red. Are there more red or green apples? ______

Name ______________________

Standardized Test Prep
Chapters 1–24

Choose the best answer for questions 1–5.

1 Which fraction tells what part of the group is yellow?

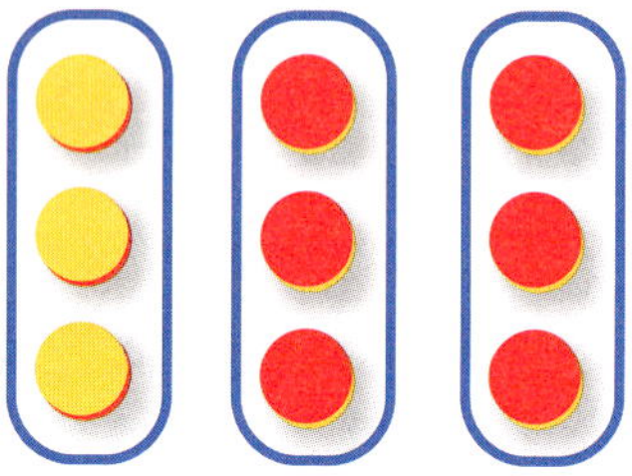

○ $\frac{1}{2}$ ○ $\frac{1}{8}$ ○ $\frac{1}{3}$ ○ $\frac{1}{4}$

---

2 Which is true?

$\frac{4}{5}$

$\frac{2}{5}$

○ $\frac{4}{5} < \frac{2}{5}$ ○ $\frac{4}{5} > \frac{2}{5}$

○ $\frac{4}{5} = \frac{2}{5}$ ○ $\frac{2}{5} > \frac{4}{5}$

---

3 Jonathan has 3 blue beads and 2 yellow beads.
What part of the group of beads is yellow?

○ $\frac{1}{5}$ ○ $\frac{5}{5}$ ○ $\frac{3}{5}$ ○ $\frac{2}{5}$

4

$$\begin{array}{r} 51 \\ +\ 40 \\ \hline \end{array}$$

○ 11 ○ 81 ○ 90 ○ 91

5

$$\begin{array}{r} 21 \\ -\ 18 \\ \hline \end{array}$$

○ 3 ○ 4 ○ 17 ○ 39

Show What You Know

6 Draw 8 circles. Color $\frac{1}{4}$ green.

Draw 12 circles. Color $\frac{1}{4}$ blue.

Hannah Hen's Kitchen

By Linda Cave Illustrated by Lisa Campbell Ernst

This book will help me review fractions.

This book belongs to ____________________.

Hannah Hen liked to bake.
She made some cornbread.

"That smells good," said Danny Dog.

"Very good," said Cassie Cat.
"May we have some?"

"Yes, I love to share!

You can have ____________, Danny Dog.

You can have ____________, Cassie Cat.

And I can have ____________.
Then all the cornbread will be gone."

Draw lines to show how Hannah Hen will cut the cornbread.

"That smells good," said Danny Dog and
Cassie Cat.
"Very good," said Paulie Pig.
"May we have some?"

"Yes, I love to share!" said Hannah Hen.

"We can each have ___________.
Then all the cornbread will be gone."

Draw lines to show how Hannah Hen will cut the cornbread.

"That smells good," said Danny Dog and Cassie Cat.
"Very good," said Paulie Pig.
"Mmm, good," said Gary Goat and Kathy Kid.
"May we have some?"
"Yes, I love to share!" said Hannah Hen.

"We can each have __________.

Then all the cornbread will be gone."

Draw lines to show how Hannah Hen will cut the cornbread.

"That smells good," said Danny Dog and Cassie Cat.
"Very good," said Paulie Pig.
"Mmm, good," said Gary Goat and Kathy Kid.
"Tasty," said Sally Sheep and Martin Mule.
"May we have some?"

"Yes, I love to share!" said Hannah Hen.

"We can each have ___________.
Then all the cornbread will be gone."

Draw lines to show how Hannah Hen will cut the cornbread.

"Oh, no," said Danny Dog.
"Harry Horse and Cora Crow are coming."
"If we give them cornbread, we will

each have ____________," said Hannah Hen.
"That is too little," the animals said.
"We don't want a part of one.
We each want a whole one."

Willie Wolf's Bakery
Cornbread
Cornbread
Cornbread
Cornbread
Willie Wolf's Bakery
"Anybody hungry?"

Name ______________________________

Mysterious Message

Use your reasoning skills to solve the message below. Shade the fractional parts of words to figure out the mystery message. Write the letters you shade in order on the lines below. Good luck!

Stretch Your Thinking ▪ Give directions that use fractional parts of words to spell your name.

Name ____________________

Challenge
Fractional Parts

1 How many sixths should be shaded to show the same amount as $\frac{1}{3}$?

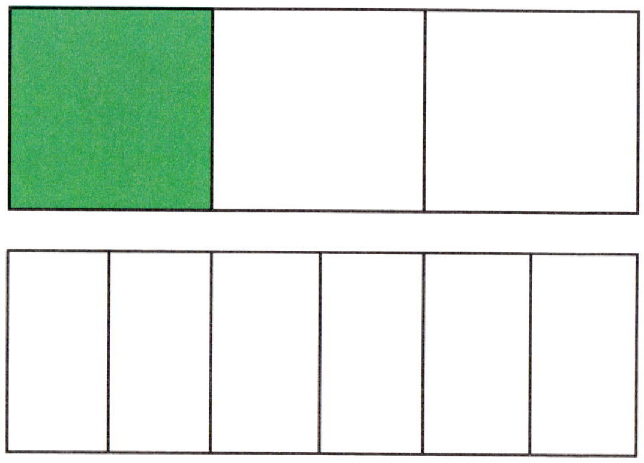

$\frac{1}{3}$

$$\frac{1}{3} = \frac{\square}{\square}$$

2 How many fourths should be shaded to show the same amount as $\frac{1}{2}$?

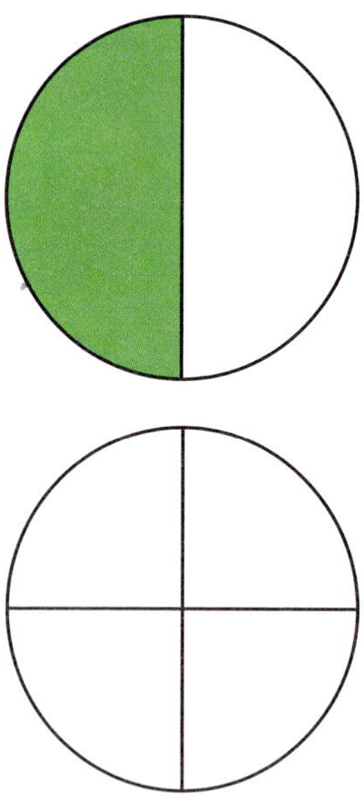

$\frac{1}{2}$

$$\frac{1}{2} = \frac{\square}{\square}$$

3 How many eighths should be shaded to show the same amount as $\frac{1}{4}$?

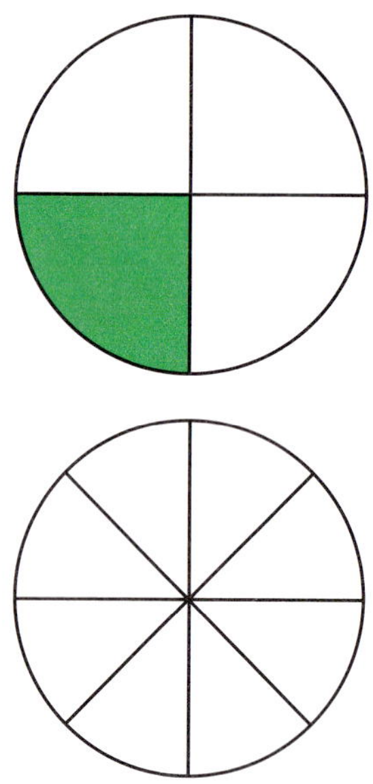

$\frac{1}{4}$

$$\frac{1}{4} = \frac{\square}{\square}$$

Name ______________________________

Study Guide and Review

Skills and Concepts

1 Write how many hundreds, tens, and ones. Then write the number.

______ hundreds ______ tens ______ ones ______

2 Write the number in different ways.

two hundred thirty-five

hundreds	tens	ones

______ + ______ + ______

______

3 Write the numbers that are 100 less and 100 more than 421.

100 less ______

100 more ______

4 Write greater than, less than, or equal to. Write >, <, or =.

123 is ______________ 45

123 ◯ 45

5 Write the numbers in order from least to greatest.

300 301 302 303 304 305 306 307 308 309 310 311 312 313 314 315

306	301	314	310

______, ______, ______, ______

6 Write the number of parts. Are the parts equal?
Circle yes or no.

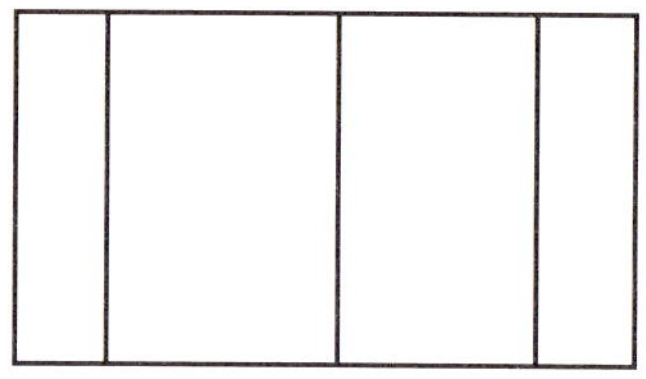

yes

no

_______ parts

---

7 Write the fraction for the shaded part.

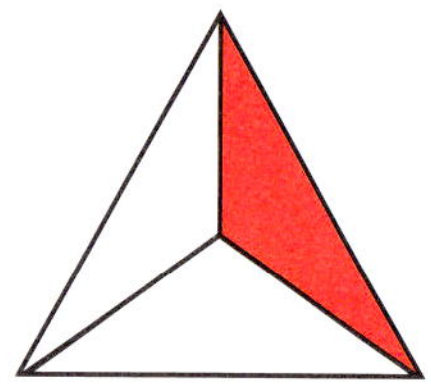

____

---

8 Write the fraction in each part. Count. Write the fraction for the whole.

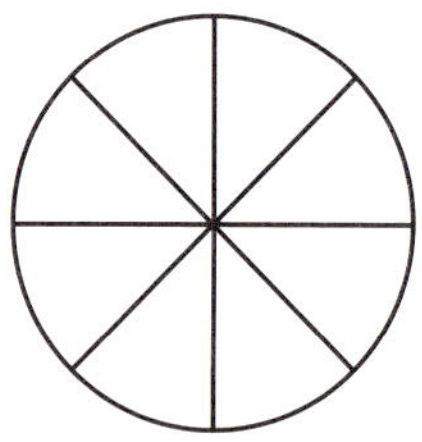

____

9 Circle the equal parts. Color to show the fraction.

$\frac{1}{6}$

---

10 Compare the shaded parts. Circle true or false.

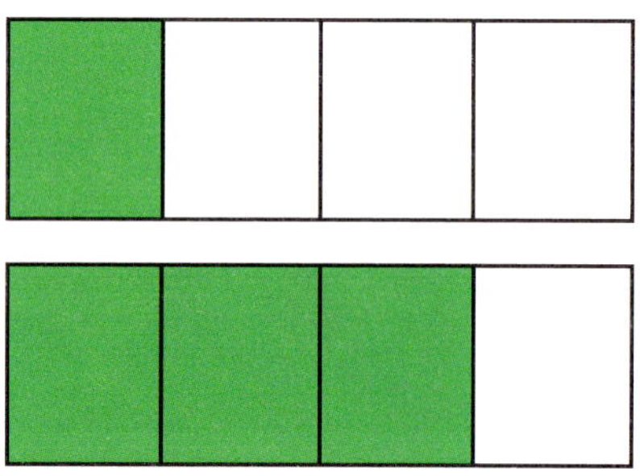

$\frac{1}{4}$

$\frac{3}{4}$

$\frac{1}{4} > \frac{3}{4}$

true false

Problem Solving

11 Find the pattern. Write the rule. Continue the pattern.

Dion sees a pattern in the numbers 235, 239, 243, 247.

The rule could be count ________________.

235, 239, 243, 247, _______, _______, _______, _______

Name ______________________________

Hats Off!

Wendy saw a group of football players standing on the sideline.

- One-third of the players were wearing helmets.
- There were more than 7 players in the group.

Draw a picture to show the possible number of players in the group. Circle the number of players in the group who were wearing helmets.

Show your work.

Name ______________________________

Mighty Math Carnival Countdown • Compare and Order

1. Click .
2. Click .
3. Click T.
4. Play 5 times.

Practice and Problem Solving

Write >, <, or =.

1. 432 ◯ 423
2. 299 ◯ 300
3. 509 ◯ 509
4. 97 ◯ 970
5. There were 350 people at the fair. Then 100 more came. Now how many are at the fair?

   ______ people

6. There were 781 cars in the lot. Then 100 cars left. How many cars are left?

   ______ cars

7. **Reasoning**
   Circle the one that is closest to 987.

   885 886 887

Name ______________________________

PROBLEM SOLVING ON LOCATION

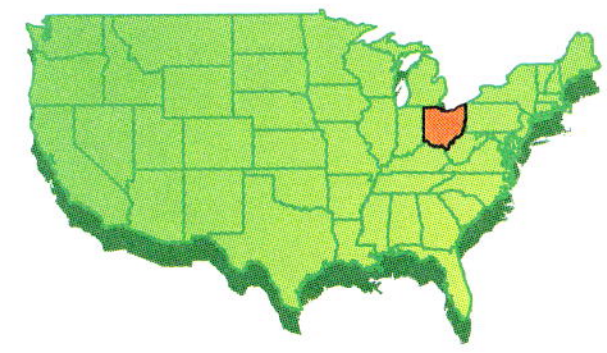

At the Market

At the farmers' market in Findlay, Ohio, you can buy fresh fruits and vegetables all summer long!

Show different ways to make a fresh fruit salad. Use 12 fruits in all. Write the numbers.

Use more apples than pears.

Apples	+	Grapes	+	Pears	=	12
	+		+		=	12
	+		+		=	12

Use fewer apples than grapes.

Apples	+	Grapes	+	Pears	=	12
	+		+		=	12
	+		+		=	12

Use more grapes than pears.

Apples	+	Grapes	+	Pears	=	12
	+		+		=	12
	+		+		=	12

Name ______________________________

Problem Solving on Location

At the Seashore

People love to collect seashells on
the beach at Cape May, New Jersey.

Some children share their seashells equally.
What fraction of the shells does each child get?

Use ● to solve. Draw to show your work.

2 children share 12 seashells.

Each child gets $\frac{\square}{\square}$ of the shells.

---

3 children share 12 seashells.

Each child gets $\frac{\square}{\square}$ of the shells.

---

4 children share 12 seashells.

Each child gets $\frac{\square}{\square}$ of the shells.